succeeding

as a
practice
management
team

the experts share
their secrets

Second edition

edited by Barry Coward

HEALTH PRESS

Succeeding as a Practice Management Team
First published 2006
Second edition March 2008

Text © 2008 Barry Coward
© 2008 in this edition Health Press Limited
Health Press Limited, Elizabeth House, Queen Street, Abingdon,
Oxford OX14 3LN, UK
Tel: +44 (0)1235 523233
Fax: +44 (0)1235 523238

Book orders can be placed by telephone or via the website.
For regional distributors or to order via the website, please go to: www.fastfacts.com
For telephone orders, please call +44 (0)1752 202301 (UK and Europe),
1 800 247 6553 (USA, toll free), +1 419 281 1802 (Americas), or
+61 (0)2 9351 6173 (Asia–Pacific).

The publisher, the author and the contributors have made every effort to ensure the
accuracy of this book, but cannot accept responsibility for any errors or omissions.

A CIP record for this title is available from the British Library.

ISBN 978-1-905832-42-2

Coward B (Barry)
Succeeding as a Practice Management Team/
Barry Coward

Typesetting and page layout by Zed, Oxford, UK.
Printed by Fine Print (Services) Ltd, Oxford, UK.

Printed with vegetable inks on fully biodegradable and recyclable paper manufactured
from sustainable forests.

444   001
Low emissions
during production

Low
chlorine

Sustainable
forests

contents

about the author

Barry Coward
Practice Manager

After a career in the Royal Navy serving in submarines and ultimately commanding a nuclear submarine, during which he was awarded the OBE, Barry Coward started out as a practice manager in 1993. In 1997 he took on the challenge of managing the start-up, with the founding general practitioner, of a new practice right from scratch, developing it into a thriving organization that now has six GPs plus supporting staff in purpose-built premises.

Barry also chaired the local practice managers' forum in South Oxfordshire, a position he has held through the run-up to the new general medical services contract, and more recently the county-wide Oxfordshire Practice Managers Committee. He has lectured widely on practice management issues. Barry and his wife live in a small village in Oxfordshire.

Abbreviations

BMA: British Medical Association
CfH: Connecting for Health
DES: directed enhanced service
DoH: Department of Health
GMC: General Medical Council
(n)GMS: (new) general medical services
PBC: practice-based commissioning
PCO: primary care organization
PCT: primary care trust
PMS: personal medical services
QOF: Quality and Outcomes Framework
SHA: strategic health authority

introduction

Barry Coward

The practice management team

It is sometimes difficult, when a member of staff has just rung in sick, last night's computer back-up has failed, the patients' toilet is blocked and a complaint has just landed on your desk, to remember that your purpose in life is to enact the next phase of the Grand Plan. In recent years, the NHS has been full of Grand Plans – the NHS Plan itself, national service frameworks, guidelines, audits, reviews, local development plans, improvement plans – so much so that they have lost much of their value. The task in any practice is to try and make sense of it all and turn the theory into reality.

The new GP contract, which was voted through by GPs in 2003 and came into effect in 2004, at last recognized the vital and wide-ranging role of management in general practice. A competency framework was published that defined the management functions necessary in any well-run practice, the headings of which are listed in Table 1. This is an enormous agenda to cover.

These competencies are broken down into three layers of activity:
- administrative
- managerial
- strategic.

For example, under the heading 'Reception', the three layers are defined as described in Table 2. Thus, implicitly, the framework also introduced the idea of the management matrix, with the various functions being covered by a small network of people within the practice.

Only the most exceptional manager could meet all the competencies defined in the framework, but a good management team should be able to cover all the functions required at all three levels. This book is therefore

Table 1

Practice management responsibilities

Practice operation and development
- Primary healthcare team meetings
- Development plans/reports
- Clinical services
- Care pathways
- Liaison with secondary/tertiary care providers
- Strategy formulation
- Innovation
- Clinical audit
- Organizational audit
- Clinical effectiveness/evidence-based practice
- Resource allocation
- Professional development
- Research

Risk management
- Health and safety
- Fire safety
- Risk assessment
- Significant event audit/reporting
- Infection control
- Confidentiality
- Ethics
- Occupational health
- Poor performance
- Disaster planning

Partnership issues
- GP time management
- Locums
- Partnership meetings
- Partnership agreement

- Partnership changes
- Taxation
- Continuing professional development requirements

Patient and community services
- Reception
- Information
- Clinics/health promotion
- Complaints
- Community liaison
- Patient protection
- Community nursing
- Social services
- Working partnership
- Networking with colleagues from other practices

Finance
- Petty cash
- Payroll and pensions
- Invoice payment
- Insurance
- Monthly accounting
- Annual accounts
- Claims, targets, quality payments
- Drawings
- Quarterly statements
- Bank and accountant
- Cash flow, budgets
- Staff budgets
- Planning information
- Service budgets
- Deficiency register
- Resource negotiation

Human resources
- Staff management
- Staff meetings
- Rotas and work
- Recruitment and selection
- Induction and training
- Employment practice
- Disciplinary and grievance matters
- Performance review
- Pastoral care

Premises and equipment
- Supplies
- Equipment
- Facilities management and maintenance
- Facilities provision
- Security
- Project management (equipment/premises)

Information management and technology
- Patient records
- Data management
- Data security
- Data interpretation and manipulation
- Hardware maintenance
- GP links
- Crisis management
- Project management

Population care
- Health needs assessment
- Service performance indicators
- Strategic delivery planning
- Service prioritization
- Resource negotiation

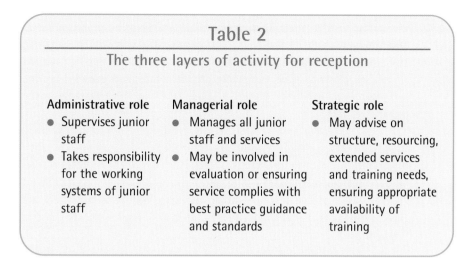

Table 2

The three layers of activity for reception

Administrative role	Managerial role	Strategic role
• Supervises junior staff	• Manages all junior staff and services	• May advise on structure, resourcing, extended services and training needs, ensuring appropriate availability of training
• Takes responsibility for the working systems of junior staff	• May be involved in evaluation or ensuring service complies with best practice guidance and standards	

designed to assist all members of the team to succeed in their roles. Each chapter has been written by an expert in the field. Our aim is to help management teams make things happen – better than that, to make good things happen. This book does not set out to be a management theory book, as there are plenty of those around, often gathering dust on the shelves. This is a book a new manager or administrator in general practice (and that includes GPs, nurses and other healthcare professionals) can read, and the more experienced can dip into.

The practice management tasks

The management team has five fundamental tasks:
- keeping the show on the road
- improving on what you have now
- responding to the changing environment of the NHS
- planning ahead
- making decisions.

Keeping the show on the road

Keeping the show on the road can, on occasions, absorb all the team's efforts. A member of staff suddenly off sick, a problem with the computer system and a difficult complaint at the same time can tie up the key members of the team completely. But keeping the practice running must be the team's first priority. I sometimes need to remind myself that solving such immediate problems takes precedence over the erudite and edifying paper I was drafting on practice-based commissioning.

Improving on what you have now

A good management team will always strive to do things just a little bit better. Much of the practice should run like clockwork, but there are always things that you think could be improved. Improvements come in two forms:

- the small change that means a minor problem or niggle is solved (an improved system for tracking all those insurance reports, rewritten guidance for note summaries, a better way for the nurses to know what needs re-ordering for the treatment rooms)
- the bigger bang, which could be as big as a new clinical software system, a new phone system or a move to new premises, or something less traumatic but still significant (recruiting a GP at last to fill a vacancy, a nurse practitioner qualifying, allowing patients to book appointments online via the internet).

Evolution rather than revolution is often the best way. Staff respond better to gradual change – they find big changes scary.

Responding to the changing environment of the NHS

Even while this book was being written, things changed and drafts had to be quickly amended. (It is interesting that almost all of the references in this book – and we have tried to keep them to a small number – are to websites, not books.) The management team will have to respond to such rapid changes in the NHS. Some changes are undoubtedly for the better, some will give rise to serious reservations.

The art of management lies in turning theory into reality. The theory is often in the form of plans, guidance, mission statements, protocols, directives and regulations that contain positive words like 'stakeholders', 'investment', 'modernization', 'holistic', and set targets and objectives without saying how they are to be achieved. So-called 'plans' are often really aspirations. Good management teams change them into reality or, occasionally, tell those on high that it cannot be done.

The changes of 2003–04, when the new GP contract was introduced, seemed huge enough at the time. However, subsequent events have shown that the new contract was but one aspect of a major programme of change in the NHS. The importance of the management team being able to sustain a strategic overview, anticipate new developments and respond to them has never been greater.

Planning ahead

Planning ahead is a key to success. Although much of the work of a general practice is responding on the spot to patients' needs, this succeeds only if the team plans ahead. Some planning (the GP rota, agreeing holiday dates, even arranging the Christmas party) is routine. The management team must look ahead, identify what needs to be done and when, and then work back.

Making decisions

Managers get asked many questions. Is this overseas visitor entitled to free NHS care? Can I have Monday off? Where do you want this shelf? The more difficult ones might concern a member of staff whose performance is below standard, how much the next staff pay rise should be or what the risks might be in commissioning a new service. Decisions made at high level within the management team should be consistent; they can set precedents.

The practice management challenge

The challenge is to make it all work. Only the hard work of good management teams made fundholding function before 1997, made personal medical services contracts a success, got the new general medical services (nGMS) contract going at all and made IT systems in general practice the world's best by working closely with clinical system suppliers. That same hard work keeps practices financially viable and trains practice nurses because no national training structure exists.

There will be days when you wonder if it's all worthwhile, but that is true of most jobs. Sometimes you will say to yourself 'Why do I bother?' But you will bother, and you'll solve the problem and move on.

Do people enjoy the job? Do I enjoy the job? Practice managers are a rather cynical bunch (or, they might say, realistic). Most, I think, gain job satisfaction from keeping things going well within their own practices, almost despite the NHS. Praise for the achievements of the management team is not heard often enough. But it does give me pleasure when visitors to my practice say 'This is a lovely building, and the staff are so friendly!', because I know how much work went into achieving that accolade. I offer just five guiding principles for succeeding in the practice management challenge.

- Good management is about making things happen and getting things done.
- Avoid the latest management fad – it will be history next year.
- Decide what is important and focus on those topics.
- Make decisions (ideally, good ones).
- Learn, if you haven't already done so, to say 'No' occasionally.

now and the future

Barry Coward

During the writing of this book, begun in 2005, the goalposts were being moved so frequently that it was almost impossible to keep up. Just as a chapter had been carefully crafted by its author, a new initiative would come pouring from the Department of Health (DoH) and change everything. In particular, three key projects, with the potential for generating massive changes over the next few years, emerged from mid-2005 onwards and moved rapidly to the head of the agenda:

- creating a patient-led NHS
- practice-based commissioning (PBC), particularly with the change in full implementation date from 2008 to 2006
- the 2006 White Paper *Our health, our care, our say – a new direction for community services.*

The first edition of this book took us up to, and included, the 2006 White Paper. The second edition now covers further developments up to early 2008. Probably the most significant of these is the work of Lord Darzi and the 'Our NHS, our future' review. An interim report was published in October 2007; the outcome of the full report, when published, may well attempt to shape the NHS for a further decade.

In this ever-changing environment, the chapters that follow are designed to assist management teams both in keeping general practice running and in implementing the constantly renewed and wide-ranging agenda. We have tried to 'future-proof' the text; however, with things constantly changing, organizations springing up and disappearing overnight, names changing and contracts being amended, that has been a difficult task.

This chapter, first drafted in the halcyon days of mid-2005, originally sat at the end of the book and mused quietly on what might be coming along. Now the future of the NHS, and general practice within it, is so important to management teams that the chapter sets the scene for the whole book. Fortunately, since the significant changes of 2005-06, further major shifts in policy have not, as yet, gone beyond the talking stage, and it has instead been a period of implementation. In particular, the reconfiguration of primary care organizations (PCOs) in England was implemented on 1 October 2006 – a massive change which may take up to 3 years to settle down.

One major lesson to emerge during the drafting of the second edition of this book is how much has changed in detail over just 2–3 years. Many of the fundamentals remain the same, which is comforting, but so many facets affecting those fundamentals have changed significantly. Examples include:

- the massive re-organization of English primary care trusts (PCTs)
- the devolution of the responsibility for delivering the English National Programme for IT to strategic health authorities in 2007
- the issues which arose over the future of the General Practice Administration System for Scotland (GPASS) from 2006 onwards.

The challenge for any management team is to try to stay abreast of those changes that matter.

The NHS is a political football, kicked backwards and forwards between the two main political parties ever since 1947. Thus, any forecast of the medium-term future of the NHS would require clairvoyant prediction of political trends in the UK – an impossible task. Nevertheless, as we passed the second edition of this book for printing in early 2008, it did seem that the thinking of the two main parties was moving along broadly similar lines, the differences being mainly ones of detail.

It would be very easy to write two, completely different, opening chapters for this book. One would be the upbeat, on-message chapter full of words such as 'stakeholders', 'challenges', 'forward-looking' and 'patient-centred'. But this is a book about management, and good management is about reality, so an opening chapter about reality is more appropriate. However, no attempt will be made to solve all the problems of the NHS – that would take another complete book.

Commissioning

A major theme of the 2006 White Paper was the shift of services from the hospital to the community setting. The target is 5% over 10 years, which does not sound a lot but could be significant in reality.

PBC clearly has a vital part to play and, if it is managed competently, practices and locality groups have the opportunity to control how this happens. However, it has taken much longer to get off the ground than anticipated and there is still a lot to learn about how much it can deliver.

People

The NHS is about people, and always will be. It is about people providing healthcare for the people of our nation. The problem is that there are not enough people to provide the healthcare – and probably never will be.

So the first challenge for the practice management team is to provide a working environment that is attractive to healthcare professionals so that they feel drawn to join your organization in the first place, and to stay thereafter. For without enough of the right people, no practice can survive.

The second challenge is to continue to be innovative in the use of people. Practice staff often respond well to taking on greater responsibility, if they are well trained and supported. For example, practice nurses enjoy the variety of dealing with minor ailments if they know they can always call on a GP for a second opinion, and receptionists now commonly also work as phlebotomists, take blood pressures and record smoking habits, among other things.

> strike a **balance** between doing everything by the **book** and day-to-day **functioning**

Against such progress, very sadly, is ever-greater regulation. Every time something goes wrong within the NHS, the stable doors have to be banged shut with more regulation and bureaucracy. This makes it more difficult for staff to work in an innovative way and simply, to get the job done. Practice management teams need to continue to strike a realistic balance between doing everything 'by the book' and enabling the practice to function on a day-to-day basis.

Part-time GPs

Full-time nurses and reception staff have probably been the exception for a very long time. The full-time GP is rapidly becoming rarer as well, and this trend is likely to grow. With more female GPs, often with family commitments, part-time working is often preferred.

Another change is that portfolio working will become increasingly common. Already, part-time partners may work 1 day a week as a locum (or even as a salaried GP) elsewhere, just for a change of pace and scene. Doing a couple of weekend sessions of choice for the out-of-hours service can fill the income gap.

The options for GPs have widened. The picture of the 'traditional' partner, who works 4.5 days a week in the practice and plays golf on his half day, is rapidly fading into the past. In its place is the part-time GP, many of whom are female, with a wider range of possibilities, and with much greater potential for control over the work–life balance. In addition, working hours are geared ever more to childcare arrangements. These considerations do not fit at all with the government's desire to see practices opening for longer hours.

Patients

Patients undoubtedly now expect more of the NHS. At one time, a resigned fatalism to having to wait for everything was probably common. Now that waiting times have been reduced, be it for a GP appointment or an operation, the public expects more from the NHS. The early 2000s saw a political climate in which the public wished to see more money invested in the NHS in return for results. In the years to 2010, the public will be looking for those results and the patient's perspective is being measured through an increasing number of surveys of service satisfaction.

In looking for results, the government has set 'choice' as a key characteristic of the NHS. Patients are able to exercise choice in two areas:
- GP practice (choice equals competition amongst practices)
- secondary care provider (choice equals competition among hospitals).

Demographic trends are quoted as influencing many aspects of society, but none more so than health (and pensions!). An increasing number of older people will hope or expect that a smaller number of younger people look after them in their old age. As has already been pointed out, there are not enough healthcare professionals today, and the pressures can only increase in the future.

The 2006 White Paper was based on a major consultation with the public. The mechanisms by which the public at large can influence the provision of services have expanded, and many new developments now include a formal public consultation process.

Access to primary care

Under the 2004 GP contract, GPs were able to opt out of overnight and weekend responsibility for patient care, and the majority did so. Core working hours are, by contract, 08.00–18.30 Monday–Friday.

However, the government is now keen to see general practice more like supermarkets, ideally open 24/7, or if not 24/7, then earlier in the morning, later in the evenings and at weekends as well.

Having said that the second edition of this book takes us to 'Our NHS, our future', this particular topic of opening hours is becoming a battleground in waiting between the government and doctors. The desires of the government (and the public) will not easily be reconciled with the doctors and nurses who are, in any event, shortage commodities, unlike supermarket checkout operators, who wish to have a reasonable family–work balance and who are becoming increasingly limited in the hours they can work by childcare constraints. Very few childcare organizations in the community (as opposed to in big hospitals) offer childcare outside core working hours.

Competition and private providers

Increased competition, including the use of private providers, is firmly on the agenda. If choice of general practice is a reality (setting aside, for the moment, the problems of home visits for patients who choose to register with a practice away from where they live), practices will have to compete to attract patients. Patients equal money. Money equals job security for GPs and staff. Lose patients because your service is not good enough and some jobs may have to go. What is your view on evening working now?

And if GPs won't do it, maybe a private provider will? But the doctors and nurses who might be employed by a private provider are drawn from the same pool as those who work for you now. Whose terms and conditions are more attractive?

On the other hand, the ability to put patient care services out to tender under PBC may already be leading to cheaper but improved services, the savings from which can be ploughed back into further patient services. Thus, competition and the increasing use of private providers will raise new issues for management teams to tackle.

Public health and treatment of chronic conditions

Catch a cold and you can see a pharmacist for medication to relieve the symptoms. Cut your finger and it does not matter too much who stitches the wound or where it is done. Develop diabetes and, all of a sudden, continuity of care becomes important. Suffer from hypertension, coupled with chronic depression and occasional bouts of irritable bowel syndrome, and not only does continuity of care matter, but it should also be holistic. In such cases, someone needs to look at the whole picture, balance the treatments for the various conditions and get the drug combinations right.

With public health, particularly smoking, obesity and sexually transmitted infections, and the treatment of long-term conditions high on both the health and political agendas, it is paramount that primary care continues to provide holistic care to patients. Turn general practices into 'patient shops' and all that is lost.

So there is likely to be a delicate balance between 'instant' services for one-off ailments and the holistic care provided by general practice for longer-term or complex conditions.

While these days people can rarely speak of 'my bank manager', they still want to refer to 'my GP'.

Locality groups

PBC points to locality groups of practices. These will grow in power and influence, and will represent true locality interests within the much larger areas covered by, for example, English PCTs. They will both commission services and provide them. They represent one of the big changes in primary care under the new agenda. Involvement in the locality group will become a key part of the management of a practice.

The commissioning role can be achieved through an association of practices based on a non-legal memorandum of understanding or similar agreement, supported by formal, minuted meetings. The provider role requires a formal legal structure, which could be based on a company or partnership structure.

IT

The National Programme for IT, now renamed Connecting for Health (CfH), is covered in the chapter on 'IT in general practice' (page 41). Whether the programme will fulfil all its aspirations remains to be seen, but some of the work of the early years is now generating results in the form of Choose and Book, GP2GP and the Electronic Prescription Service. At the time of writing, the holy grail of the National Care Record Service is still some way off.

Even if the final scope of the programme is somewhat watered down from its early, idealistic concepts, there is no doubt that even greater use of IT will be essential for all practices. Thus, all practice management teams must continue to invest in IT skills, either through recruitment or through developmental training of current staff. Even then, in all except the very largest of practices, the practice team is unlikely to have the full spectrum of expertise needed, and a willingness to employ a local computer expert when necessary will be money well spent.

The paper-light practice has been around for several years, often constrained by the fact that most information from other providers still arrives on paper and has to be scanned. This is changing and, in future, most information, both patient-related and management-related, will be received in electronic format.

Money

Until there is another major change in the way that general practice is financed, practice income will have reached a plateau, with the 2005–06 increase in the value of the Quality and Outcomes Framework (QOF) points having worked its way through to end-of-year outcomes. As is explained in the chapter on finance (page 55), the government, having put more money in, has now set itself a thinly disguised target of clawing money back out of general practice owing to perceived 'over performance'.

Future financial development will now depend on cost-effective bidding for enhanced services and any savings from PBC that are reinvested in primary care services.

Affordability

A major flaw in the 2000 NHS Plan, which has continued through so many policy documents since and has remained a major omission from the 2006 White Paper, is that affordability is mentioned nowhere.

Funding is allocated to PCOs largely on a capitation basis, weighted for a number of factors, deprivation being one. From that allocation, PCOs are charged with implementing government policies, many of which are 'must do's', or influencing whichever assessment tool (e.g. star ratings), is now in vogue. The ever-increasing list of services that PCOs must commission, the widening array of advisers, auditors, liaison services, arm's-length bodies and so on, just add to the costs.

In 2005–06, the bubble wall started to thin, and the following years certainly saw a reality check on everything the government wished to happen, in particular when the NHS went through the deficit crisis of the mid-2000s, which put a temporary hold on many plans. The way policy has developed and been promulgated appeared, for a decade, to be completely isolated from the financial and workforce resources available. Such luxury is not accorded to the management teams in general practice; policy development must be built on a bedrock of financial and personnel considerations.

The future of practice management

Although in the late 1990s some questioned the need for practice managers at all, practice management is here to stay. Indeed, the role is likely to grow. GPs and nurses have enough work to do looking after patients and they want a management team behind them that can give them the tools to do the job. That team will have to be ever more:

- financially astute
- skilled in IT
- accomplished people managers
- wonderful at translating plans into reality
- innovative
- competent
- knowledgeable
- appropriately qualified
- adequately and appropriately rewarded – and they will need a great sense of humour, too.

Given these attributes, the management team can achieve results, gain satisfaction, enjoy the job, and provide an excellent service for patients and their own staff alike.

The NHS environment evolves and changes; the basic tools of good management remain unaltered. The chapters that follow aim to give management teams the necessary tools to do the job, to succeed in running a first-class practice, and to take pride in what is achieved.

the management team

Barry Coward

The management team consists of some or all of the following people:
- partners or GPs with nominated leads (e.g. staff, finance, clinical governance)
- the manager, normally called the practice manager, but may be business manager, chief executive or similar
- senior reception or patient services manager
- nurse manager, senior nurse or nurse practitioner
- senior dispenser
- specialist deputies or assistants (e.g. IT, accounts, administration).

Some members of the team devote most of their time to doing the management job; others are clinicians who also spend some time on management functions.

The practice manager

The practice manager should be the management team leader and the linchpin of the practice. A good practice manager will set the whole ethos of the practice.

Today, practice managers need expertise in many areas; for example:

> the **practice manager** is the **linchpin** of the practice

- strategic planning
- customer (patient) services
- understanding the NHS
- finance
- human resources
- IT
- premises
- health and safety

- public relations
- law.

And all this is in addition to just plain management!

Finding managers with this range of skills is not easy. Practice managers have a wide variety of backgrounds and will continue to do so, and managers recruited from outside the NHS will often bring a fresh perspective. While a good practice manager is likely to have a number of key attributes (Table 3), the most important criterion for any practice manager is that they should 'fit in with the team'.

> a **practice manager** should **fit in** with the **team**

Practice management is not an easy job and it can be lonely. The practice manager sits between the partners and the staff. Sometimes, it can lead to conflicts of loyalty, and there are times when the practice manager has to stand firm on something and please nobody.

Table 3

Key attributes of a good practice manager

- Competence
- Makes decisions
- Fairness
- Consistency
- Respects a confidence
- Gets on with people

Partners

The skills of managing a partnership are covered in greater detail in the chapter on 'Working with partners' (page 101). However, it is important never to forget that the partners own the business and, thus, have a say in how the business is run!

The partners are usually, though not necessarily, also GPs; nurse partners are still rare, practice manager partners perhaps less so. Obviously, GPs trained as doctors, not managers. Nevertheless, some GPs develop in-depth expertise in areas such as finance or IT, while others have a natural flair with people. These skills can be harnessed to add greater strength to the management team.

On the subject of strength, it is easy to get into a situation where the practice is reliant for certain functions entirely on the practice manager. It is, therefore, important for the partners to understand the management of the practice at the strategic level in order to see the practice through a period when the practice manager may be absent, for example, through sickness.

Independent contractor status

The partners are independent contractors. Under the old general medical services (GMS) contract, they were contracted individually by the Secretary of State to provide medical services. Now contracts are between groups of GP performers and PCOs. Nevertheless, the legal status of partners remains unchanged.

This status affects how the management team operates. The management team works for the partners, and not the PCO or the NHS. The task of the management team is to run the practice in accordance with the partners' wishes, while meeting contractual obligations to the PCO and thus to the NHS. Furthermore, practice staff are employed by the partners, not the NHS.

Independent status also means that, when needed, the management team can move quickly. Decision-making takes place within the practice. Decisions do not, for example, have to be subjected to a round of draft papers, scrutiny by committee or approval by the appropriate Director. This makes even the largest of practices relatively self-contained; this is one of the great strengths of general practice. The teams are tight-knit, know each other well and, if everything else is running smoothly, can respond quickly to something new or unexpected.

> **independent status**
> means that the **team** can
> move **quickly**

The management matrix

As already outlined, the management team will comprise many members of the practice team: some will be full-time managers and some will undertake management tasks as only a relatively small element of their role.

Formal and rigid hierarchical management 'wiring diagrams' are no longer appropriate in many management structures, and general practice is no exception. To a greater or lesser extent, management topics such as staffing issues, IT, finance, law, and health and safety will involve all team members, and a rigid demarcation of roles is not usually the best way of working.

Furthermore, people will move in and out of the management matrix. A project may involve a particular combination of team members working together towards an agreed objective. For example, introducing a new appointment booking system may involve reviewing software options, product selection, modifying ways of working, staff training, finance, installation and setting to work.

> make clear who is responsible for particular actions

It must be made clear who is responsible for taking particular actions. In this case, the practice manager may place the order for the supply and installation of the software, and the senior receptionist may set up the training programme. Similarly, restructuring the way diabetes clinics are run would require significant input from the GP lead on diabetes until the new system is up and running, but would then reduce to a simpler monitoring role.

> the management matrix is a rather fluid structure

Not only is the management matrix a rather fluid structure, but its agenda changes continuously. Priorities are reassessed, new ideas come along, other ideas are dropped or an event occurs that has a major impact on plans (e.g. a key member of staff leaving). Any plan of work for the management team must, therefore, be constantly reassessed, time scales adjusted and financial provision rescheduled.

the management team

Qualifications and experience

Nowadays, full-time managers in general practice must be appropriately qualified. On the other hand, it is unrealistic to set rigid criteria as to what those qualifications should be. While paper qualifications should always be taken into account, they should be considered part of the total 'package' any particular manager offers. One thing is certain, however: previous broad management experience is a prerequisite.

> develop a **portfolio of knowledge** and **update** it **constantly**

Any new practice manager, or any other member of the management team whose primary role is as a manager, must develop a portfolio of knowledge and constantly update that knowledge through a programme of continuous professional development.

Although knowledge may be acquired through a formal qualification, much can be gained by personal learning and research. Today, practice managers have to assimilate so many new things so fast that waiting for a course to be offered does not work. Reading, gaining understanding, looking things up on the internet, asking others and networking are often not only as effective as sitting in a classroom, but quicker.

Salaries

GPs and nurses who also have management roles are paid according to their clinical skills and qualifications. However, the pay scales for managers in general practice are derived differently and have never been wonderful. Even the job assessments (and thus the pay banding) in the 'Agenda for Change' put practice managers in completely the wrong bracket – this is not currently mandatory for general practice, but it does serve as a guide. Many people outside general practice just do not understand the importance of the role.

The competency framework for practice management, as defined in the nGMS contract documentation, is bringing about change. A practice manager who is taking on a significant proportion of the 'strategic role' within the competency framework has a wide-ranging and responsible job requiring appropriate remuneration. This should be band 7 or 8A on the pay scale: that is, more than £30 000/year (2007).

Leadership and motivation

Although leadership is a rather underrated concept these days, books about leadership fill the libraries of the world. Leadership is about setting examples, about taking the lead and showing the way.

leadership is about **setting examples**

Key members of the management team set the standards for the practice. Like it or not, they set the example which others will follow, consciously or subconsciously.

- A partnership in which the partners are unsupportive of each other will set the tone for the whole practice.
- A practice manager who is unresponsive to staff problems will cause resentment and ill-feeling.
- A senior nurse who demonstrates good clinical practice (ideally without acting like an old-fashioned matron) will be followed by the other nurses.
- An IT manager who sorts out computer problems quickly so others can get on with their work helps to establish an ethos of 'let's get the job done, and done well'.

Gathering intelligence

Gathering intelligence sounds like a military operation, and to an extent it is. The NHS has moved rapidly to a situation in which the 'powers on high' think that, as soon as something has been published on a website, everyone knows about it and will act to bring the next great initiative into force. It is therefore vital to scan websites, such as those for the DoH, CfH (formerly the

gather **intelligence – scan websites** regularly

National Programme for IT), the British Medical Association (BMA) and your own PCO, regularly.

In addition, PCO staff and others are continually circulating new information to practices by email. So rather than being swamped with paper, the management team now are swamped with emails!

Emails need sifting and weeding as thoroughly as paperwork. The old rule about dealing with a piece of paper only once applies equally to emails; bin all the junk right away, and delete redundant emails regularly (including the 'Deleted' box!) to ensure the system does not clog up.

Equally important is gathering information about the NHS 'environment', both nationally and locally. The management team needs to understand the wider context in which they are working, particularly with so many new initiatives being announced on an almost daily basis. Sources of information include:

- journals/magazines, such as *Pulse*, *GP*, *Doctor*; it is worthwhile for managers to subscribe to some of them in their own right
- a plethora of websites, including the DoH (www.dh.gov.uk)
- newsletters, such as those from the BMA, General Practitioners Committee (GPC) and Local Medical Committee (LMC)
- PCO Board, Professional Executive Committee and LMC minutes
- networking with colleagues, either face to face or by email
- local forums (e.g. practice managers, GPs)
- the national press and news websites such as the BBC's
- the *GP Bulletin*, published by the DoH.

The importance of networking with colleagues in other practices has never been greater. Such is the scope of the challenging agenda facing practices that the chance to bounce things off other managers, to benefit from the experience or expertise of another manager and even to have the proverbial shoulder to cry on occasionally has never been more important.

The courage to get it wrong

Development is about trying things. Occasionally, the management team will need to try something that may not work and must have the courage to do so. Most things, if well thought through in the first place, will work or can be made to work with a bit of fine tuning. Occasionally, something does not work and the idea has to be abandoned. It is, however, essential to keep the other members of staff informed throughout the process.

Also, from time to time, the management team will embark on something new in the firm belief that it will work – and it does not. Again, it is important to have the courage to say 'Sorry, we got it wrong'. The management team must acknowledge mistakes, learn from them and move on.

A management team that will never take a risk will not get very far. Nevertheless, risk needs to be assessed and balanced. Clearly, a major financial investment that carries a significant risk of not working is not prudent. However, a modest investment in, for example, some new software, which turns out not to do the job expected, should be acknowledged as a lesson learned, but not taken as a reason for never trying something new again.

development is about
trying things

Enjoying the job

Finally, team members need to enjoy the job – despite the NHS. The NHS places great pressures on those who work for it. Management teams must not let those pressures get on top of them and must, as the cliché goes, be mellow and stay cool.

Further reading and references

Department of Health: www.dh.gov.uk

Connecting for Health: www.connectingforhealth.nhs.uk

British Medical Association: www.bma.org.uk

the NHS environment – can we use it to make a difference?

Virginia Bushell
Practice Manager

Have the changes made since the NHS Plan was introduced made a difference to the care patients receive? And what about the targets, such as the 4-hour wait limit in A&E? Targets have helped but they may also have distorted some clinical care. The 2-week wait for investigation of possible cancer is reassuring for the patient, but there is little evidence that treatment occurs any faster. On the other hand, the 18-week target from GP referral to treatment complete will, if achieved, make an enormous difference.

But I do not suppose that patients are the least bit interested in what a PCO is, how primary care is planned or funded, or whether GPs, consultants, pharmacists or dentists had a new contract, or have been set certain targets. 'PEC' is what chickens do. 'NICE' refers to good food. 'PbR', 'CfH' and 'HRGs' are not terms the man in the street uses. So why should they make a difference to us as members of a general practice team?

It is not essential to know these things. It is perfectly possible to offer good primary care to patients, pick the most useful guidance to inform clinical and management practice and ignore the rest. At times, it is absolutely essential for sanity's sake to take refuge from the deluge of guidance, encouragement, information and advice, and just keep your head down and do what must be done! But if we are to do a bit better for others than we have done for patients in the past, we need to be able to influence colleagues in the NHS and beyond.

PCOs are responsible for about 81% of NHS expenditure. This may not seem like such an opportunity considering that most PCOs are struggling to balance the books. However, national strategies do not support the status quo. They are consistently concerned with access, patient choice, services closer to home, maintaining independence and looking at the broad agenda of health, not just illness. Such strategies might just result in care that is effective, valued and even lower cost. Frequent admissions via A&E cannot represent the best service that can be offered. General practice teams have never had a better opportunity to make a contribution to the quality of care patients receive. To make a difference, it is important to understand the language, the incentives and disincentives, the rules, and how to make systems and procedures work.

teams have never had a better **opportunity** to **contribute** to the **quality of care**

The environment in which practice management teams must work is always changing, driven by what has become a highly political strategic agenda. A Labour government in the late 1990s and early 2000s transformed the nation's view of the NHS. It is now so high on the political agenda that whichever political party is in power over the next 10 years, it is likely that the strategy will be broadly the same, although the systems for delivering it may well change. There will almost certainly be some further changes in nomenclature, and some big changes have happened, for example the huge re-organizations of strategic health authorities (SHAs) and PCOs in England, first announced in mid-2005 and implemented from October 2006. In the meantime, the following is a brief summary of the possibly useful, if diverse, pieces of the jigsaw puzzle which, with further exploration, fit together to make a surprisingly coherent picture of a strategy for change in the NHS.

understand how **systems** and **procedures work**

the NHS environment – can we use it to make a difference?

The National Health Service

With devolution, the NHS was split into separate national structures, each controlled by the respective national executive. Each nation has its own plan (for example 'Renewing the National Health Service in Scotland' and 'The NHS Improvement Plan' in England), but they are all committed to significantly increased spending on healthcare. These services are almost entirely funded by general taxation and national insurance contributions.

The *Health Service Journal* is essential reading for current analysis of the NHS. It is *the* journal read by NHS managers.

Primary care organizations

Eighty percent of NHS funding now goes to PCOs in their various forms (for example, local health boards in Wales or PCTs in England). This alone is a very good reason to understand PCOs, and the incentives and disincentives under which they operate. What does your PCO spend on average per head of population? How is it apportioned across services? Does it seem a reasonable mix to you, or can you think of other, better (more care/more effective care/more responsive care) ways of distributing the funds? Look at PBC! What are the targets the PCO must achieve? What are the penalties for failure?

PCOs are answerable to a higher management level within the national structure, e.g. SHAs in England.

Healthcare resource groups

Healthcare resource groups (HRGs) are acute care groups that are classified under about 600 headings, grouped within specialties to assist comparison, planning, costing and analysis (see www.ic.nhs.uk/casemix).

NHS trusts

There were over 600 NHS trusts in the UK in 2007–08. Most of their income comes through services commissioned by PCOs. NHS Trusts provide secondary care, which is accessed generally by referral from a GP. As well as the hospital-based specialist services, NHS Trusts provide mental health services, learning disability services and ambulance services.

Primary Care Contracting

Supporting PCTs in England, Primary Care Contracting (PCC) was formed to assist the development of new local contracting arrangements in primary care. It has a network of expert advisors, underpinned by their website (www.primarycarecontracting.nhs.uk), newsletter, helpdesks and event management functions in order to support commissioners across a wide range of PCT functions with timely and robust advice.

Working in Partnership Programme

The Working in Partnership Programme (WiPP) was launched in 2004 under the nGMS contract to support general practice with capacity-building resources and strategies. In its first 2 years, WiPP designed, developed, tested and delivered a range of valuable tools, working in collaboration with over 100 NHS and lay organizations. These include, for example, a database of good practice, and advice about the development of the role of healthcare assistants (www.wipp.nhs.uk).

Professional Executive Committees

Professional Executive Committees (PECs) of PCOs are key decision-making forums, and practice teams are critical to their success. By statute, membership must include:
- the chief executive
- the director of finance
- one or two social services members
- one or more public health members
- 'professional' members.

membership of a PEC is an excellent opportunity to gain a better understanding of the NHS

Professional members include medical practitioners, nurses and others who, in the opinion of the trust, reflect the functions carried out by the trust (likely to include clinicians from other professional groups, such as therapists and pharmacists). Practice managers are not specifically included, but in a number of PCOs they have been appointed to the PEC as non-voting members. Membership is by appointment, and provides an excellent opportunity for members of the practice management team to gain a better understanding of the NHS and to exercise some influence on how NHS income is spent, as well as to maintain awareness of opportunities and threats on the horizon.

Local Development Plan

The Local Development Plan (LDP) was a 3-year plan produced by PCOs within a national planning framework. That meant that it had to include specific commitments to meet national requirements, but also to meet the health needs of the local community.

The names change and LDPs seem, in 2007–08, to be evolving into a hierarchy of strategic plans, operational plans and local delivery plans, all of which are quite difficult to keep up with.

Local authorities and personal social services

PCOs are working closely with local authorities, partly because it makes sense as good health depends on many factors, and more particularly because responsibility for personal social services lies with the DoH, though organizationally social services are delivered through county councils. There are already many areas where budgets have been pooled, and the boundaries between social care and healthcare are blurring. That has implications for the management, coordination, funding, risks, accessibility and quality of care. What kinds of opportunities and threats does this closer relationship bring?

NHS walk-in centres

Originally, 42 NHS walk-in centres were developed as a 3-year pilot scheme and this has now expanded to more than 80. Improving access is a consistent theme in NHS strategy. Continuity is no longer as important a feature of general practice as it has been historically – no more 24-hour and 365-day cover, no evenings and no weekends. While opportunities to see your 'own' GP at convenient times are limited, services like NHS24 and NHS Direct are available 24 hours a day, and the new pharmacy contract will deliver much of the routine advisory and medication monitoring roles historically carried out in general practice. In GMS and personal medical services (PMS) practices, GPs are increasingly being encouraged to bridge the gap between primary and secondary care. The walk-in centres offer another option to patients. Do these changes indicate that perhaps the traditional monopoly of general practice over primary health is changing?

The National Institute for Health and Clinical Excellence

Until April 2005, this agency was two bodies: the National Institute for Clinical Excellence (NICE) and the Health Development Agency. The merged agency is still known as NICE and publishes guidance in the following areas (www.nice.org.uk):

- technology appraisals of medicines and treatments
- clinical guidelines on the appropriate treatment and care of people with specific diseases and conditions
- public health intervention guidance on the types of intervention that help reduce disease risk or that help to promote or maintain a healthy lifestyle
- public health programme guidance for the promotion of good health and the prevention of ill health, focusing on particular topics or populations
- interventional procedures guidance on whether intervention (mostly surgical) for diagnosis or treatment are sufficiently safe and effective for routine use.

National Service Frameworks

National Service Frameworks (NSFs) are a rolling programme in which service standards and performance measures are set, and implementation plans produced to raise standards and contribute to the modernization of the NHS. The NSFs cover:

- coronary heart disease
- cancer
- paediatric intensive care
- mental health
- older people
- diabetes

the NHS environment – can we use it to make a difference?

- long-term conditions
- renal services
- children.

Connecting for Health

CfH is a huge undertaking, costing over £6 billion, to create, among many other functions, a national computerized patient record (see page 52). The programme includes electronic referrals (Choose and Book) and the Electronic Prescription Service (EPS).

It is worth finding out who your local project manager for CfH is and asking for an explanation on how the system will work – email question-and-answer sessions work very well. Although major concerns have been expressed from various quarters, this programme is going ahead and is now starting to address some significant problems in communication and coordination in the management of complex care. You should also investigate how it will affect general practice, in order to ensure the benefit is gained from all the encouragement (financial and intellectual) that is being invested.

> investigate how **Connecting for Health** will affect **general practice**

Screening programmes

PCOs, together with SHAs, will be responsible for securing effective screening programmes. The established National Screening Programme (i.e. cervical screening, breast screening and antenatal infectious disease screening) is to be extended to include, for example, bowel cancer. PCOs are expected to fund this programme, but where is the flexibility? The expense should not be underestimated. These commitments will require investment, in competition with many other priorities.

The Quality and Outcomes Framework

The QOF links general practice activity to many of the national priorities for clinical care. Most practices are now fully conversant with the targets and have noted the relationship between the target disease groups and the NSF. While practices have struggled to incorporate NSF targets into their day-to-day workload, the QOF provides direct incentives to do this work, and where practice teams understand how to achieve the targets this is proving a very effective strategy. Ongoing changes to the QOF will allow additional clinical areas to be included, with a consequent improvement in patient care.

Payment by Results

Payment by Results is a national policy to introduce standard tariffs for treatment (financial flows). The process began in April 2003 with prices set for just 15 elective HRGs (see page 21), extended to a further 33 HRGs in April 2004 and then to full coverage in April 2005.

The measure of hospital activity, which used to be called a 'finished consultant episode', is now known as a 'spell'. The intention is that care is commissioned on a cost and volume basis. In other words, you pay for what you get (see page 95). Early experience with spells mirrors the experience in general practice, in that it takes quite a while to refine data into information and to understand what the numbers actually mean, who the services are provided for and why, and where one spell finishes and another begins. This is important to those working in general practice teams, because in order to commission care, the rules must be understood. The HRG system is now being updated annually.

> in order to **commission** care, you need to **understand** the **PbR rules**

Practice-based commissioning

PBC (see page 93) was introduced across the country from April 2005 for those practices wishing to take up the challenge. Practices generate referrals for elective care, and are best placed to judge whether alternatives might be more cost-effective and meet patient needs better (as well as being consistent with the NHS strategies and NSFs).

As with many changes, the first hurdles were understanding the information and testing the boundaries for exercising new opportunities and responsibilities. Just deciding starting points has not been easy. How will we know if we are successful? The management of patients whose route into hospital does not involve general practice is a difficult area. Are we developing the skills, information and support we need to exploit these opportunities? Sustained success will mean better services for patients, practices reaping proper rewards for their efforts, and PCOs confident about the level of risk they are carrying and realistic about the potential benefits – particularly, but not exclusively, financial benefits.

Patient-led NHS

In mid-2005, *Creating a patient-led NHS – Delivering the NHS Improvement Plan* was published. It defined the way forward for the second half of the 10-year NHS Plan. The first 5 years were spent building capacity and capability; the second 5 years are, under the NHS Improvement Plan, to deliver quality, best value for money and a truly patient-led NHS. This key document also heralded the huge re-organization of SHAs and PCTs in England, which came into effect on 1 October 2006, as well as emphasizing patient choice as a key element of future developments.

The 2006 White Paper *Our health, our care, our say – a new direction for community services* was published in January 2006. A number of important themes emerged:

- a shift of care from the hospital to the community setting, which had already been predicted by the increasing emphasis on PBC as the way forward
- great emphasis on prevention
- introduction of competition into the primary care setting with plurality of providers, including commercial companies, increased patient choice and pressure to extend opening hours
- a greater say for the public in commissioning decisions and the development of services in general
- ... but a complete absence of any discussion of affordability.

Skill mix

It is now necessary to look at ways to distribute the increasing workload appropriately within the practice team. One of the risks in the NHS strategy

> without **good staff**, the **best strategy** will **fall** at the **first hurdle**

is that, because this is happening throughout the system, there are not enough skilled people to go round. Training and development take time and should be under continual review. Without good staff, the best strategy will fall at the first hurdle.

Agenda for Change

Trying to get consistency in the pay and conditions for NHS staff has always been a mammoth task, and there is a recognized tendency towards pay drift. Agenda for Change provides for a national pay spine and a standardized approach to job evaluation. Although general practice staff are not included in this initiative, some practices are interested in retaining comparability with the NHS payment systems.

Long-term conditions

These are the focus of considerable attention, for good reason. Just 5% of inpatients, many of whom have a chronic condition, account for 42% of all acute bed days, and only about 50% of medicines are taken as prescribed (from *Supporting People with Long-term Conditions*, DoH, January 2005). There is a widely accepted perception that we can probably do better by the patients by providing more systematic care before acute hospital admission becomes a necessity.

Out-of-hours services

Now that PCOs are responsible for providing emergency primary care services outside the core services, there is considerable interest in solving what has become a difficult problem. If patients do not get the service they want in one part of the system, they tend to go to another part of the system. It is not in the interests of PCOs for patients to go to A&E, where they may be treated by the hospitals, which are paid for each spell. There is a growing appreciation that the out-of-hours services were underfunded, and also that a richer mix of services is needed to respond to the high expectations of patients.

Pharmacy contract

The pharmacy contract introduced in April 2005 requires three levels to be provided by community (i.e. not hospital-based) pharmacists: essential, advanced and local enhanced services. Pharmacists will:

- provide repeat dispensing
- offer advice to improve public health, such as healthy eating, stopping smoking and regular exercise
- dispose of unwanted medicines
- provide medicine-use reviews for those with long-term conditions.

This is an interesting development for general practice. It will reduce some of the pressures on practices and it will provide an interesting comparison for patients. One aim of the contract is to secure longer opening hours with accessible health advice that is readily available on the high street.

Electronic Prescription Service

The electronic transmission of prescriptions is another strand of CfH. The first pharmacy systems have been tested, full roll-out is due in 2008 and EPS will become an essential requirement for the pharmacy contract.

General practitioners

It is useful to appreciate some of the changes that have occurred in the availability of GPs (excluding registrars, retainers and locums) between 1994 and 2004.

- The numbers of GPs increased by 1.5% a year.
- The percentage of part-time GPs increased from 13% to 25%.
- The number of GP registrars increased by 77%.
- The number of female GP registrars increased by 94% (from 60% in 2004).
- The number of GPs aged over 60 rose from 6.6% to 8%.
- The number of GPs aged under 30 fell from 1.9% to 1.6%.

The GP population is increasingly made up of part-time professionals, predominantly female, and it is an ageing population. Training has increased to bridge the inevitable gap, and changes in the GP contract should help to make general practice increasingly attractive.

Further reading and references

The National Institute for Health and Clinical Excellence: www.nice.org.uk

National Audit Office: www.nao.org.uk

Choose and Book: www.chooseandbook.nhs.uk

the NHS environment – can we use it to make a difference?

the legal environment

Linky Trott
Edwin Coe Solicitors

The management of any employment relationship, particularly the dismissal of an employee, can be a legal minefield for the uninitiated and, while incurring legal expenses is always unattractive, specific, focused advice from an experienced employment lawyer can help avoid potentially expensive potholes.

There are four stages to any employment relationship:

- recruitment
- initial employment
- the ongoing employer–employee relationship
- the termination of the employer–employee relationship.

Every stage carries with it statutory obligations, some of which are obvious, such as a responsibility not to discriminate, and some of which require a set process, such as the 'letter, meeting, appeal' process that must be undertaken prior to most dismissals or during any formal disciplinary process.

The main statutes and regulations are: the Equal Pay Act 1970; the Sex Discrimination Act 1975; the Race Relations Act 1976; the Disability Discrimination Act 1995; the Employment Rights Act 1996; and regulations providing for equality of treatment notwithstanding an individual's part-time or fixed-term status, religion, belief and/or sexual orientation. In addition, anti-age discrimination legislation was introduced in October 2006. Thus, all

every stage of employment carries statutory obligations

recruitment and employment decisions should be made on the basis of objective business requirements and an individual's qualifications and experience alone.

Recruitment

Legislation, principally that relating to discrimination, applies to the recruitment process from the initial placing of an advertisement to the interview.

Ensure that, when the advertisement is read as whole, there is no discriminatory effect. This is easy to identify in terms of sex, race and religion, but be alert to disability discrimination and age discrimination, which make phrases such as 'young, energetic secretary required' potentially problematic.

A deadline for applications should also be stated in the advertisement.

To identify those who will be interviewed, objective business criteria should be set in advance of considering applications; the use of a standard application form will assist the filtration process. Application forms should include the usual requirements for details, such as name, address and contact numbers, qualifications, previous experience and referees. In addition, it should give applicants an opportunity, if they wish, to detail any disabilities that might affect their application and, if so, whether or not there are any reasonable adjustments that could be made to assist them during the interview process. This is illustrated by the case of a candidate who suffered from light-sensitive eyes and who was requested to remove her dark glasses, which she later alleged affected her ability to perform in the interview.

job advertisements must **not** be **discriminatory**

It is permissible to ask applicants if they have been convicted of any criminal offences that have not been 'spent', as provided for under the Rehabilitation of Offenders Act 1974. Criminal records can be checked through the Criminal Records Bureau (CRB). The procedure for and cost of CRB searches can be found on the CRB website (www.crb.gov.uk).

Examples of standard application forms can be located through the Advisory, Conciliation and Arbitration Service (ACAS) website (www.acas.org.uk).

If the interview pool remains too large and it is not possible to narrow the criteria further, restrict the pool by some objective means such as the first five applications received that meet the requirements.

During any interview process, get to know your candidate by focusing on their previous experience and qualifications, the nature of the role and their aspirations; steer away from personal issues, such as marital status or whether or not they have any children, which would be discriminatory. To ensure that all applicants are treated equally, prepare a standard interview procedure, such as discussing CVs and then asking all candidates the same previously prepared questions.

> prepare a standard interview procedure

Initial employment

Having identified your preferred candidate, offer them the job and provide details of the standard terms and conditions of employment. Offer letters should state that the offer is subject to the following conditions.

- The terms and conditions included must be met. These must provide the information required by Section 1 of the Employment Rights Act 1996 (see Table 4).
- Satisfactory references must be received. There is no prescribed way of taking references, but a standard reference form asking direct questions of work referees, such as 'what was their reason for leaving?', 'would you employ this person again?' and 'please give an assessment of this person's general conduct, quality of work, timekeeping, attendance, work ethic' is advised. Written references should be followed up with telephone references.
- The necessary documentation detailed in the Asylum and Immigration Act 1996 must be produced. It is an offence to employ a person not entitled to work in the UK. The statutory defence is to demonstrate the existence of one of a listed range of documents.

Table 4

Information that must be included in the terms and conditions of employment

- Names of the employer and employee
- Date of commencement of employment
- If the contract is a fixed-term contract, the end date
- Job title and summary of duties
- Place of work
- Usual working hours: the Working Time Regulations 1998 impose numerous obligations on employers, including the maximum number of hours per week an employee can work, the number and length of rest breaks to which an employee is entitled and specific provisions relating to those working nights; they are comprehensively outlined on the Department for Business, Enterprise and Regulatory Reform (BERR) website (www.businesslink.gov.uk)
- Details of holiday entitlements; all employees must receive at least 4 weeks of paid holiday a year
- Salary, including intervals of payment
- Details of disciplinary and grievance procedures (see pages 35 to 37), though it should be specifically stated that these procedures are not contractual
- Whether or not there is a contracting-out certificate under the Social Securities Pensions Act 1975 relating to state pensions; the answer to this is likely to be no, but this should be stated
- Details of pension arrangements; practices that employ five or more individuals are obliged to provide access (but not to contribute) to a stakeholder approved pension scheme
- Details of sick leave and pay; there is no obligation to provide contractual sick pay, but if an employee is eligible for statutory sick pay this should be paid
- Whether or not there are any employee collective agreements; the answer is likely to be no, but this should be stated
- Details of notice to be given by either party; a probationary period for new employees is advisable during which any notice period is short (e.g. 1 week)

Copies of the documents should be kept. It is discriminatory to prescribe which documents should be produced, so a copy of the relevant list of documents should be obtained from the Home Office's Border and Immigration Agency (www.bia.homeoffice.gov.uk).

- Satisfactory evidence of qualifications and/or membership of professional organizations must be produced.

Staff handbook

In addition to the standard terms, it is good practice to create a staff handbook. As a minimum, this should contain an equal opportunities policy, health and safety policy, email and internet use policy if you provide access to these facilities and wish to reserve the right to read or monitor an employee's use of them, and a confidentiality statement expressly stating that the practice's patient lists, for example, are confidential. Sample policies can be obtained from the ACAS website (www.acas.org.uk) and the Health and Safety Executive (www.hse.gov.uk), which also provides a useful outline of health and safety law that is beyond the scope of this chapter.

> create a staff handbook

Employer–employee relationship and termination

Annual performance appraisals should be held to address strengths and weaknesses and to review goals. Comments from both sides should be documented. Confrontational issues, such as an unhelpful attitude, should be discussed, but an appraisal is not the same as formal disciplinary action.

Grievances

If any employee has a grievance, they are obliged to raise it under the statutory grievance procedure. The requirement is to notify the employer in writing, and in response the employer must call a meeting to discuss the grievance, advising the employee of their right to be accompanied. It is also necessary to provide a right of appeal against any decision made.

Constructive dismissal

There is much confusion about the term 'constructive dismissal' and how it differs from unfair dismissal. In order to lodge a claim for unfair dismissal, an employee must demonstrate that they have been dismissed. When an employer tells an employee to leave, this will be clear. Under some circumstances, however, a tribunal will find that when an employee has resigned, he/she has in fact been 'dismissed' (constructive dismissal), because the employee's resignation was in response to a fundamental breach of contract by the employer.

A fundamental breach could, for example, be the reduction of an employee's salary without his/her consent. Less obviously, an employee may allege a fundamental breach of the implied term of mutual trust and confidence. This may be alleged by employees who have been bullied or victimized or where employers have allowed such conduct to continue.

The most common types of claims brought by employees are unfair dismissal, wrongful dismissal (essentially breach of contract), discrimination/victimization, unfair redundancy and unlawful deductions from wages. Unfair dismissal is by far the most common, but employees are unable to make such a claim until they have been employed for 1 year ('protected employee'). In calculating that year, a tribunal will add the employee's minimum statutory notice period of 1 week.

Protected employees can only be dismissed for one of the reasons outlined in the Employment Rights Act 1996. The most important of these are: capability, misconduct and redundancy.

Capability

When new systems, procedures or equipment are introduced, employees will require specific training. If all reasonable measures have been taken to assist employees and they still have difficulty, they should be given clear and ample warning to improve. All discussions on the subject should be documented, but if it becomes necessary to address the issue on a formal footing, employers must follow the 'letter, meeting, appeal' process outlined in the following section.

the legal environment

Misconduct

When formally addressing an issue of misconduct, employers must follow the 'letter, meeting, appeal' process, described below.

If there is a member of staff who is consistently late in the morning, a reasonable first step would be to discuss the reasons for this in a relatively informal setting.

If the employee continues to be late or other conduct issues arise, such as taking long lunch hours or leaving early, the matter must be addressed through a formal disciplinary process. When calling any disciplinary meeting (whether for misconduct or capability) the employee must be notified in writing of:

- the issues arising and the supporting evidence
- the fact that there will be a formal meeting to discuss and hear any representations
- the date and time of the meeting
- their right to be accompanied by a colleague or union representative.

The employee should be given time to consider the letter before the meeting. Following the meeting the employer should consider the appropriate sanction and tell the employee, who must be advised of their right to appeal and of their right to be accompanied to the appeal meeting.

The above procedure is referred to as the 'letter, meeting, appeal' procedure, and it is essential to ensure that this procedure has been undertaken before the imposition of any formal disciplinary sanction and before dismissal for any reason, even if it is a dismissal by the expiry of a fixed-term contract or retirement.

> the 'letter, meeting, appeal' procedure is essential

Failure to do this will result in an automatic finding of unfair dismissal, whatever the underlying justification.

Redundancy

The procedure to adopt in a redundancy situation is summarized in the following example.

If an employer has three secretaries and introduces new technology, with the effect that they are not all fully occupied, one of the secretarial rolcs may be determined to be redundant. This satisfies the test of redundancy in that fewer secretaries are required to undertake the work generated by the business. A tribunal will not examine a management decision of this nature in any great detail, but employers should be prepared to justify, in general terms, that there is indeed no requirement for three secretaries. Any proposal to replace the 'redundant' secretary means that it is not a redundancy situation.

All three secretaries must be treated the same, and objective selection criteria should be used to determine who is affected by the redundancy of one of the roles. Objective criteria would include 'last in, first out', length of service, disciplinary record and qualifications. All the secretaries should be scored against those criteria and the one with the lowest score will be the one whose continued employment is at risk.

use **objective selection criteria** to **determine** who becomes **redundant**

The individual at risk should be given a letter advising of the redundancy of one of the secretarial roles and advising that they have been identified as the individual whose employment is thereby at risk. This letter will be the letter in the 'letter, meeting, appeal' process referred to above and should invite the person to a meeting to discuss the redundancy and their selection, and advise of the right to be accompanied.

At the meeting, the reason for the secretary's selection should be outlined and any representations they have to make in connection with the proposed redundancy and their selection should be considered. This is the consultation process, and it should be approached with an open mind without any final decision having been made.

Once the meeting has been held, a final decision may be taken. If it is decided that the employment should be terminated on the grounds of redundancy, the secretary should be given notice of the termination of employment and advised of the right to appeal. Redeployment of a redundant employee must be considered during the consultation process and during any notice period.

Further reading and references

Criminal Records Bureau: www.crb.gov.uk

Advisory, Conciliation and Arbitration Service: www.acas.org.uk

Home Office: www.homeoffice.gov.uk

Health and Safety Executive: www.hse.gov.uk

Department for Business, Enterprise and Regulatory Reform (BERR): www.businesslink.gov.uk

IT in general practice

Lynn Gentle
IT Manager

Great advances in the use of IT in general practice have been made in the last few years, and the IT system is now absolutely essential in any practice.

Clinical systems have been developed to assist clinicians in healthcare delivery, health promotion and meeting the targets set under the new GP contract. The administrative functions within a practice, such as registering patients, producing medical reports and booking appointments, can be built into most clinical systems, enabling the system to be integrated.

This chapter will outline the major functions now available in most systems. It will also serve as a checklist that management teams may wish to use to assess their own systems and identify areas for further development.

Major functions of clinical systems in general practice

Appointment systems

Most clinical systems contain a built-in appointment system that integrates with the patient's record. However, some practices have an add-on appointments system, which has a number of additional features. Appointment management is such a key part of any practice that full use of the appointment system's features is vital.

The appointments template also enables audits of, for example:

- 'did not attend' (DNA) rates (patient education and behaviour changing)
- length of wait between arriving and being seen
- length of consultations (useful for nGMS patient experience indicators; the average length of routine booked appointments should be at least 10 minutes, and in open surgeries, GPs should average at least 8 minutes with each patient).

Some systems enable concurrent appointments with a nurse and GP to be made. Also, some systems maintain separate appointment back-ups so that, in the event of a clinical system failure, a list showing pre-booked appointments can still be viewed or printed. In addition, computerized systems, by assessing appointment usage, have enabled many practices to implement advanced access appointment systems (in the nGMS) and meet DoH targets of waiting times of less than 48 hours to see a GP or 24 hours to see any healthcare professional. The appointments screen in some systems may also be able to display alerts that nGMS indicators have not yet been achieved for that patient.

full use of an appointment system's features is vital

A more recent development has been a system that enables patients to check themselves in via touch screens, allowing reception time to be used more efficiently. Many systems now have the facility to link to patient display boards to call patients into the consulting rooms.

Consulting

Clinical systems allow clinical data to be coded and analysed using Read codes (4 byte, 5 byte or Clinical Terms Version 3). An understanding of the standard datasets of Read codes is especially important to ensure consistent data entry across a practice in order to achieve points in the QOF. The patient record, correctly coded, also forms the medicolegal record of patient care.

Standardized data entry is important for audit. Quick and consistent data entry can be achieved by the use of a template, which also acts as a guide to ensure completeness of chronic disease reviews. Templates also have the advantage of enabling new users to record data in a standard manner. Nevertheless, it is advisable to have a practice policy on the information that should be routinely coded.

Free text entries, which cannot usually be used in audits, can be entered into the consultation details to give a full clinical picture. Some systems also enable clinicians to add details, such as drawings (e.g. to indicate the site of a breast lump), to the patient's notes. Automated consultation entries are possible with some systems.

Most of the functions of the system can be accessed via the consultation screen or its equivalent. This means it is possible to view referral letters, scanned documents and electronic pathology results during a consultation, which obviates the need to use the patient's paper records and enables practices to work 'paper-light'.

> standardized data entry is important for audit

Prescribing and dispensing

Computerized systems have obvious advantages in prescribing and dispensing, for both repeat and acute prescriptions.

- The system can indicate interactions and alert prescribers to possible allergies.
- Some practices can set up their own prescribing formularies, which can assist cost-effective and generic prescribing according to PCO policy and incentives.

Other useful functions are audits of prescription use and the prescribing of expensive drugs. Dispensing practices may use the clinical system for stock control and drug ordering, as well as label printing. Issuing post-dated prescriptions may be useful for patients who consistently overdose, or those who require weekly dosset boxes.

Some systems support nurse prescribing, which may be an important consideration as practices develop their nurse-led services.

Searches, audits and reports

Data can be extracted and analysed from clinical systems for a variety of uses; for example, meeting quality indicators for the nGMS, monitoring levels of clinical care and reviewing prescribing activities.

It is important to ensure data entry is consistent throughout a practice for it to be retrievable and to give accurate audits of activity.

Integrated word processing

Most clinical systems now contain integrated word processing functions that enable mail-merging of patient details, both demographic and clinical.

Medical dictionaries are available that can be integrated into clinical systems word-processing software. In addition, voice recognition software can be useful for entering clinical information, or dictating letters.

Pathology and radiology results

safe data transmission is achieved through **encryption**

Electronic transmission of results into GP systems is available from most suppliers. Pathology results should conform to the national pathology bounded Read Code list and should be integrated into the clinical record. Safe transmission is achieved through encryption of the data.

Clinical record attachments

Scanned images can be attached to patient records (e.g. discharge letters). Spirometry and ECG results can also be attached to clinical records. Some systems also enable electronic document management (creating, storing, searching and sharing files such as letters, records and images) to assist workflow within the practice. This is becoming more important as practices become more paper-light.

Patient information and clinical decision-making

Some systems provide up-to-date patient information leaflets that can be printed as required. Prodigy (http://cks.library.nhs.uk) has been devised not only to provide such leaflets, but also to support clinical decision-making.

Portable technology

Remote access or the use of portable technology to view and record clinical data, for example on home visits, is becoming increasingly available.

Registration

When a patient registers at (or leaves) a practice, the information can be stored and passed electronically to local registration departments. This allows central NHS databases to be kept up to date and ensures that patient records are moved to the correct practice. Similarly, patient demographics can be updated and transmitted daily. From mid-2008, the local registration departments will be by-passed in this process and practices will link directly with the Personal Demographic Service (PDS).

Managing systems

Paper-light status and data security

Practices should follow the *Good practice guidelines for general practice electronic patient records* (version 3.1 dated July 2005: www.dh.gov.uk/en/ Publicationsandstatistics/Publications/PublicationsPolicyAndGuidance/ DH_4008657), a practice can apply to its PCO for paper-light accreditation in accordance with local policy, and most practices will now have done so. The back-up of data and secure storage of back-up media are important factors to consider, and full business continuity plans must be put in place to ensure patient safety is not compromised in the event of unforeseen circumstances. Tape validation services are available, which make it possible to check whether the back-up tapes contain restorable data.

> practice staff must be aware of the importance of data security

Storing data in secure folders on the server rather than on PCs may be preferable, as it is easier to ensure that they are backed up, and servers arc lcss likcly to bc stolcn. All clinical systems need to be accredited to RFA99 or above, which will ensure that an audit trail exists within the system. Practice staff must be aware of the importance of data security relating to passwords, data protection and the Caldicott principles (see page 51).

Critical updates and antivirus software

Clinical system suppliers are usually responsible for ensuring critical updates, patches and antivirus software are installed on the server(s). In addition, it is important that all PCs are protected with up-to-date antivirus software.

Some PCOs may provide support for network, desktop and hardware maintenance.

System support

System suppliers should be able to access your server remotely and securely via N3 to provide troubleshooting, diagnostic and maintenance support. The suppliers provide a fault logging and monitoring system to track issues reported by practices.

Intranets

Some practices are able to set up an intranet on their network to assist with the sharing of documents within a practice (e.g. policies). Effective use of intranets can save a great deal of time and make information accessible to anyone in the practice at the click of a mouse.

IT funding

In the nGMS, it is now the responsibility of the PCO to fund baseline practice IT, including hardware and clinical system purchase and support costs. However, the practice may be required to fund the purchase of any software or additional hardware. Some software for standard office applications can be purchased under the NHS licensing scheme; the software is supplied at the minimal cost (www.licencetoclick.com), but this software must be used for NHS purposes only.

As IT replacement is now the responsibility of PCOs, practices may not be expected to insure their IT equipment, but this should be discussed with your PCO and insurer. PCOs are also responsible for ensuring that an appropriate IT infrastructure is in place for use with CfH applications. You may have to fight hard for funding, because PCOs often try to use the IT budget as an easy way of saving money.

> **IT replacement** is the **responsibility** of the **PCO**

Disposing of redundant IT kit needs to take into account the wiping or destruction of hard drives to ensure no confidential data can be retrieved. Hard drives should be wiped using a certified piece of software (this will incur a licence fee). If redundant IT kit is going to be reused outside the practice, it is important that no NHS-licensed software or operating systems remain on the PC.

GP Systems of Choice

When the National Programme for IT was first rolled out, the concept was that all English practices would ultimately be supplied with standardized clinical software to facilitate information management and technology (IM & T) adoption, a concept tried in Scotland with the GPASS system. Ultimately, common sense prevailed and it was realised that the clinical systems already being used by practices were highly developed and very sophisticated. The GP Systems of Choice (GPSoC) concept is that practices can now retain, and PCOs will fund, accredited systems, which will themselves meet agreed national standards.

Information Management and Technology Directed Enhanced Service 2006

This short-lived directed enhanced service (DES) nevertheless has had an on-going impact on the IM & T programme in practices as it:
- included certain standards for training in practices
- included compliance with data security standards
- most importantly, required a lot of work on data accreditation
- included a requirement to work towards implementing the Electronic Prescription Service

- included, controversially, a requirement for practices to work towards remote server working.

However, practices could 'sign up' to some elements of the DES but not necessarily all. The DES seemed to be designed to achieve a big step forward in general practice IT, and then was quickly discontinued.

Business functions

Payroll and accounts packages

Software packages are available specifically for accounting purposes in general practice, and have built-in facilities for nGMS payments and for dealing with the payroll, including NHS pension payments. Today, the complexities of general practice accounts are such that IT support is essential.

Internet banking

if **BACS payments** are transmitted via the **internet,** ensure the **Acceptable Use Policy** for connection to the **NHSnet/N3** is met

Practices that use internet banking for transmitting BACS payments should ensure they meet the Acceptable Use Policy for connection to the NHSnet/N3. If this involves setting up a separate analogue modem connected to a stand-alone PC or, if the PC is on the network, that the BACS payment line is blocked to incoming traffic.

Internet and websites

Practice websites

Practices may wish to set up an internet website. The site may inform patients about the GPs who practice at the surgery, other clinicians and administrative staff, surgery times, services available and may possibly have a facility for ordering repeat prescriptions.

Some practice websites have developed systems to enable patient registration via an online form that is transmitted to the practice. The practice can either accept or reject the form in accordance with normal procedures. Routine appointments can also be released by practices, allowing patients to book themselves an appointment online; a limit can be set on the maximum number of appointments any individual can book.

Ideally, practices should conform to the NHS website guidelines (www.nhsidentity.nhs.uk) when setting up and maintaining their site.

NHS Choices

In mid-2007, a new national website was set up (www.nhs.uk) which was intended to allow patients to find out about practices, their opening times, who the doctors were, etc. Unfortunately, it was largely populated with incorrect data! In late 2007, the site was modified to allow practices to edit the information about their own practice.

NHSmail

After the demise of antiquated X400 email, an internet-based system called NHSmail has been introduced. People register to receive an email address, which stays with them wherever they work in the NHS. Individuals are then added to the national directory, which can be searched to find anybody working in the NHS. Email has now become such an essential way of doing business that all members of the management team need to be comfortable as users.

> the only **secure** email **route** for sending **Patient Identifiable Data** is from one '.nhs.net' address to another

The only secure email route for sending Patient Identifiable Data is from one '.nhs.net' email address to another.

Administration sites

Sites for practice managers (see www.firstpracticemanagement.co.uk) contain protocols and policies that can be shared with other practices.

Hospital websites

Most hospitals have websites, which provide information about the hospital as well as statistics (e.g. waiting times). Some hospitals also publish referral proformas that can be downloaded by practices for referring patients. Local clinical guidelines may also be available.

Statistics and information about each hospital trust in the country, as well as each GP surgery, can be obtained via www.nhs.uk.

Training and qualifications

European Computer Driving Licence

The European Computer Driving Licence (ECDL) is a recognized standard within the NHS, and ECDL training should be available, free, to every member of the NHS. You should check with your local training service to find out how to enrol to access the NHS ECDL portal, where training for each of the modules (e.g. word processing, databases, spreadsheets) is available as well as practice tests. The tests for each module can be arranged at local test centres (www.ecdl.nhs.uk).

Windows training

Practice staff and GPs will all require basic Windows IT skills in order to operate most clinical systems currently in use. CfH systems will require a minimum level of Windows proficiency. Training courses should also be available for practice staff through local PCOs or shared support services that cover several PCOs.

Clinical software training

When a clinical system is first installed, the supplier will offer staff training and telephone support on how to use the system. Further in-depth training (e.g. creating templates, protocols and searches) may also be offered. As functionality develops, further training is available, but is usually charged for. You will need to ask your PCO about funding.

PRIMIS+ (www.primis.nhs.uk) offers free training to help standardize and optimize recording of data on clinical systems. This is particularly important under the GMS contract.

Medical terminology courses

Courses in medical terminology may be very useful for any non-clinical staff involved in clinical data entry. The Association of Medical Secretaries, Practice Managers, Administrators and Receptionists (AMSPAR) offers courses especially tailored to primary care (www.amspar.co.uk).

Confidentiality, the Caldicott principles and clinical governance

Ideally, all practice staff should have confidentiality training, and an understanding of the Caldicott principles and clinical governance. Information governance guidelines require practices to ensure that they have security and confidentiality policies in place that adhere to the Data Protection Act (www.opsi.gov.uk; see pages 141 and 142), the Freedom of Information Act (www.foi.nhs.uk) and the Caldicott principles (www.dh.gov.uk).

> ideally all staff should have confidentiality training

IT knowledge

It is becoming essential for general practice IT systems to have wide functionality. So it is important that, to make best use of the systems, there is sufficient breadth and depth of knowledge about IT within the management team. To enable the full potential of the system to be realized, the management team must understand:

- the system as a system, and server/network functionality
- all facets of the clinical system, particularly data entry, Read codes, consultation entries, setting up standard templates, searches and audits
- appointment systems
- scanning and attaching files to patient records

- Windows and MS Office, especially Word, Excel, PowerPoint and specialized software (e.g. accounting packages)
- the internet plus NHSNet/N3, websites, Internet Explorer and MS Outlook
- data security, backing-up data and antivirus measures
- the need for staff training.

It is clear that IT expertise is now a prerequisite within every practice. Training to, for example, ECDL standard is a good benchmark for most staff, but at least two members of the management team need IT skills well beyond ECDL level.

Investment in comprehensive IT skills will reap rewards within any practice.

Connecting for Health

CfH, which manages the National Programme for Information Technology, is an ambitious programme, and management teams need to be familiar with it. In the early years, the programme received a lot of adverse criticism for the way it was being managed. Accountability for delivery of the programme transferred to strategic health authorities in 2007. The key elements of the programme are summarized below.

Over 10 years, CfH will link up IT systems within the NHS. Currently, NHS IT systems generally are unable to link up with one another and sites are maintaining many separate sources of patient data. Linking these systems will improve patient care and patient safety, as well as provide more efficient systems for staff and clinicians (www.connectingforhealth.nhs.uk).

CfH is being delivered in three clusters in England. Each cluster has its own local service provider (LSP):
- Southern – Fujitsu
- London – BT
- North, Midlands and East – Computer Sciences Corporation.

Underpinning CfH is the National Data Spine. The National Data Spine holds patient demographic data and will enable the National Care Records Service (NCRS) to be developed, which will hold all patient records. This will then enable timely access to records as required, will be controlled by tight security procedures to preserve confidentiality, and will assist with delivery of appropriate patient care.

The infrastructure that will link all NHS sites to CfH applications is the New National Network (N3). This replaced the NHSnet and will provide a more resilient service, with back-up lines and broadband-type connections, as well as a cost-effective service across the NHS. NHS sites will eventually be able to utilize N3 for telephony as well as IT. However, there are concerns as to whether N3 has the required capacity to support the system.

General practice has now been using a CfH solution called Quality Management Analysis System (QMAS) for a number of years. This enables QOF data for the nGMS indicators to be collected centrally via a website in order to determine QOF payments.

The national applications of CfH are:

- the National Data Spine, which hosts the Personal Demographic Service as well as the NCRS
- Choose and Book, which facilitates delivery of choice at the point of referral, electronic booking and electronic referral (www.chooseandbook.nhs.uk), and which really started to get off the ground in 2006
- from 2008 onwards, the Electronic Prescription Service, which enables electronic transmission of prescriptions from prescribers to pharmacists, as well as a link to the Prescription Pricing Authority
- GP-to-GP transfer of records (the ability to transfer electronic medical records when patients register with a new practice), which went live in 2007
- secure access for providers of medical care via the NCRS to a summary electronic record of every patient (e.g. out-of-hours services will be able to check whether a patient is allergic to any medication before prescribing, and the registered GP will be able to see the details of the out-of-hours consultation)
- Picture Archiving and Communication Systems (PACS), which enable radiology images to be accessed and viewed, thereby providing timely access as well as obviating the need for additional X-rays if patients attend another hospital.

LSPs are responsible for providing systems in each cluster that will link up to these national applications. This includes a system for community and child health.

In order to access any CfH clinical application, you must hold an NHS smart card. These are issued to NHS staff following proof of identity. As primary care clinical systems become compliant with National Data Spine, all users will require a smart card in order to be able to access the system.

> the **need** for **consolidated** **IT skills** will grow **ever more** **critical**

Many practices have developed their IT systems and working practices over the last few years. With the advent of CfH, the next few years will see many changes and progress in the practice of IT within the NHS to provide fully integrated systems, and the need for consolidated IT skills within the practice management team will grow ever more critical.

Further reading and references

Prodigy: www.prodigy.nhs.uk

Good practice guidelines for general practice electronic patient records (version 3.1 dated July 2005): www.dh.gov.uk/en/Publicationsandstatistics/Publications/PublicationsPolicyAndGuidance/DH_4008657

NHS information governance requirements: www.dh.gov.uk/en/Publicationsandstatistics/Publications/PublicationsPolicyAndGuidance/DH_079616), www.ico.gov.uk

Data Protection Act: www.dh.gov.uk; www.opsi.gov.uk

Freedom of Information Act: www.foi.nhs.uk

Caldicott principles: www.publications.doh.gov.uk

NHS Choices website: www.nhs.uk

NHS licensing scheme for standard office software: www.licencetoclick.com

NHS identity guidelines: www.nhsidentity.nhs.uk

Protocols and policies for practice managers: www.firstpracticemanagement.co.uk

European Computer Driving Licence: www.ecdl.nhs.uk

PRIMIS+ (free training for standardizing and optimizing data recording): www.primis.nhs.uk

The Association of Medical Secretaries, Practice Managers, Administrators and Receptionists (medical terminology courses): www.amspar.co.uk

Connecting for Health (formerly the National Programme for IT): www.connectingforhealth.nhs.uk

Choose and Book: www.chooseandbook.nhs.uk

finance

Barry Coward

Managing the finances of a general practice successfully is one of the essentials of running a practice well. Practice finances are now much more dynamic than under the old contractual arrangements, and the ability to look ahead and plan effectively is the key to success.

Nevertheless, there is one financial golden rule: 'general practice is a profit-making business' – no profit, no take-home pay for the partners. If income is down or expenses up, profit is down, which is generally considered bad news. People outside general practice find it difficult to grasp the concept of partnership finances, and why practice or finance managers talk about the GPs

> look ahead and plan effectively

having to pay for something 'out of their own pockets'. But this is the reality of a business that is owned by the partners, and what happens if additional costs are incurred with no corresponding reimbursement. Thus, the ability to say 'no' is an important attribute of the finance team.

The new GMS contract

In 2003–04, the financial aspects of general practice went through a revolution, in the form of the nGMS contract. The implications of the new finance initiatives also had a profound effect on PMS practices.

Key elements of the new contract are summarized below.

- An attempt was made to redistribute national funding on the basis of perceived patient need. Unfortunately the mechanism chosen (the so-called Carr-Hill formula), succeeded in hugely underfunding most practices, except perhaps those in deprived inner-city areas. Therefore, it had to be propped up by the 'Minimum Practice Income

Guarantee', which meant that, in the first instance, practices would not find themselves worse off. This led to the Correction Factor, which makes up the shortfall between what the practice was earning under the old contract and the core funding under the new contract.

- The concept of 'enhanced services' was introduced. These services are commissioned by the PCO, and the contracts do not necessarily have to be awarded to general practice.
- Payments for providing services, such as travel jabs, contraception and new-patient medicals (the old 'Items of Service'), were dropped and the QOF introduced instead. The QOF rewards quality achievement against target indicators, both clinical and organizational.
- New money was introduced, largely in the form of the QOF. This was expected to increase practice profits, among other things, thus resulting in a pay rise for partners; results from 2004–05 showed that many practices did indeed increase their profits initially.
- All the funding was brought together under a small number of headings, primarily the contract sum for core services, plus enhanced services and QOF income.
- Pensions for GPs were improved.

One of the complications of the new contract was that, as it was being introduced, the employer's element of superannuation funding increased from 7% to 14%. This led to complex mechanisms for introducing this funding into contracts, particularly for PMS. The financial year 2004–05 was largely spent getting to grips with the implications of this new contract and agreeing the small print of budget setting.

The contract budget

All practices will now have an agreed contract budget, whether it is for GMS or PMS. The hard work was done way back in 2003–04 and there is nothing more to be done except to maintain what was previously agreed in good shape.

The key now until the next big change, will be making sure that the core budget is correctly adjusted. The mechanism for adjusting the budget is laid down nationally for GMS, but agreed locally with the PCO for PMS. However, essentially, there are only two elements to a contract core budget adjustment:

- quarterly adjustments for changes in list size, for GMS at least, and ideally also for PMS (as agreed locally)
- the annual percentage increase in fees, if any.

Enhanced services

The core budget occupies one end of a scale; enhanced services are right at the other end, in that nothing is fixed. They are likely to change continuously, as there is much that might be done year on year.

The contracts placed by most PCOs for the financial year 2004–05 were a first attempt. The PCOs had an obligation to commit a minimum – the so-called 'floor' – to enhanced services and, for all but the most far-thinking PCOs, this consisted largely of recommissioning the services that were already in place (e.g. coil fitting, minor surgery).

There has been, and still is, scope for innovation and opportunities for PCOs or practices to stop providing some services, to reshape other services and also to start providing new services. As far as the practice is concerned, a business case must be made for each enhanced service. The trouble is that the business case may be skewed by an altruistic desire to continue to provide a service to patients. Indeed, there was plenty of evidence from 2004 that doctors and nurses continued to provide some services (e.g. minor surgery procedures) for free or had accepted a contract price lower than the nationally set prices.

The climate has changed, with some PCOs starting to be more adventurous and innovative. They can certainly consider alternative providers of certain services, some of whom will be private. As a result, practices will have to compete in a more open market. This means that the pricing of services has become a key skill. One advantage that practices still enjoy is that the fixed overheads of running the practice should already be covered by the core contract funding. Therefore, in pricing a new service, normally only the additional costs of staff, and perhaps some running expenses, plus any necessary equipment, would need to be taken into account.

Such developments have also given practices the opportunity to drop work that really does not pay.

pricing of services
has become a key skill

The true strength of the practice management team is demonstrated by its implementation of the QOF. Success requires the integration of so many facets of the practice, including finance, IT systems, data quality, clinical governance, GP and staff training, appointment management, recall systems, prescribing and ways of working, that the team must truly work as a team. The ultimate goal is that achievement of QOF requirements becomes part of the everyday activity of the practice.

The first year of the QOF in 2004–05 saw the first assessment visits by PCO teams. The visits required a great deal of preparation to produce the portfolio of supporting evidence. Much was learnt. Subsequent years should have been easier, particularly as much of the work on the management and organizational indicators had been done once and did not need to be done again. However, it has now become apparent that the QOF will be revised every 2 years. 2006 saw big changes and the precedent was set of expanding the clinical indicators with no increase in overall points, which meant more work being required just to maintain income.

The QOF is worth a great deal of money to all but a few practices, and thus has been the key to the development plans of the practice. In broad terms, the money is likely to have been invested in:

- additional staff and services to help achieve the targets
- additional GPs and staff to ease the workload of all
- additional profit, thus giving the partners a pay rise.

> the QOF is worth
> a great deal of money

Most practices will probably have opted for a mixture of all three. One measure of success, of course, is to ensure that the extra income generated more than pays for any additional staff taken on.

It is likely that most practices have already reached a plateau of points achieved, where the effort and resources required to achieve the final few extra points cost more than the additional income generated. A plateau at around 990 points out of the current QOF maximum of 1000 is a realistic goal.

Of course, it is also important to have a good in-house forecast of the anticipated income from QOF, particularly as the online forecast from the

QMAS reporting system does not become anywhere near accurate until the last 2–3 months of the financial year. Also, as the achievement money is not received until after the end of the financial year, it could have a large impact on the practice if the achievement funding is significantly adrift from the forecast on which extra investment or drawings have been based!

The QOF will continue to change with time, the first big change introduced in April 2006 having expanded the clinical areas and reduced the management and organization targets. In the future, further indicators and targets will be modified or scrapped, and new ones introduced. The challenge for the team will be to keep abreast of any changes, anticipate, prepare, plan and then achieve anew.

Many practices introduced incentive schemes, which rewarded all staff for QOF achievement. However, such schemes may already have served their purpose as the QOF has rapidly become mainstream business and a vital source of income.

Non-NHS income

Income from outside the NHS should not be forgotten. Most practices generate a useful income from activities such as insurance reports, medicals for heavy goods vehicle licences and signing certificates. Some of the work has to be done in any event, because the practice holds the patient's records and is thus the custodian of key information about the patient.

> get those who **want** the **information to pay up front**

A useful trick is to get those who want the information to pay up front, particularly insurance companies, but also patients – no money, no report. It saves doing nugatory work in the first place and saves on administrative effort chasing unpaid fees.

Practice-based commissioning

PBC is covered in more detail in the chapter on 'practice-based commissioning and related changes' (page 93). But there are two aspects of PBC which have emerged to affect practice finances directly.

- A directed enhanced service for PBC management in 2006/07, which then turned into an incentive scheme in 2007/08. The purpose was to introduce some funding into practices to pay for the clinical and management time involved in PBC, while setting targets for achieving outcomes. This has introduced an element of additional funding into practices, but a significant proportion will also have been spent on PBC management and administrative activity.
- The ploughing back of freed-up resources (FURs), some of which can be used for practice capital expenditure or to pay for developments which support the PCO's agenda, which might include staff training, piloting new services, etc. The big constraint with FURs is that the money is non-recurring.

The Statement of Financial Entitlement

The Statement of Financial Entitlement (SFE) is now the bible; it is a bit easier to read than the so-called Red Book that it replaced, but not much. The finance management team must know the SFE backwards.

From time to time, the practice will be entitled to additional payments. The finance team must make sure the practice receives all the funding to which it is contractually entitled. The PCO will not normally volunteer the funds – they must be claimed.

Reimbursement or funding may be claimed for expense such as:
- GP locum cover for maternity, paternity and adoptive leave
- GP locum cover for sickness (if the absence is long enough).

These payments come from the PCO's discretionary budget, and it is important to know the basic rules for claiming them. The trick is first to know that something is claimable, and then to work through the rules to generate a valid claim. Be tenacious – PCOs can be creative in finding reasons to refuse claims.

Future challenges

The first 2 years of the new GMS contract generated big increases in income and profits in most practices, mainly through very high levels of achievement in the QOF. In late 2005, the government set themselves a target of clawing back what they now perceived as 'over performance' in general practice – in other words, they thought general practice was paid too much! Therefore zero, or below-inflation, increases in basic budgets were the tool used, plus increasing the scope of the QOF without increasing the number of points or value per point.

Over the next few years, in terms of generating income for the practice, the challenges will be to:

- maintain high QOF points at minimum additional cost
- respond proactively to new QOF developments, so that the practice continues to benefit from the extra income
- respond to enhanced services developments, but consider the business case and consequent pricing for each service carefully before commitment
- be hard-nosed and business-like when it comes to the financial aspects of PBC.

> be **hard-nosed** and **business-like** when it comes to the **financial** aspects of **practice-based commissioning**

Expenditure

Once the income of the practice is known, or can be forecast with reasonable accuracy, then financial success depends on managing expenditure. In reality, expenditure can be divided into just three main areas – fixed and variable overheads, and discretionary expenditure – and, once the pattern is known, it will largely repeat itself year on year.

Fixed overheads

Fixed overheads are items such as electricity, telephone, insurance, business rates, rent, supplies of consumables and bank charges. By all means, shop around for the best deals but, once agreed, the costs are largely fixed and predictable. Assuming no significant changes, the electricity bill this year will be much the same as last, allowing for an increase in price.

Variable overheads

Overheads that are fixed in the short term and variable in the medium term are the largest area of expenditure, because they mainly comprise staff costs. On any day, a number of staff are employed at agreed rates of pay, and the practice is contractually committed to paying them. Over time, however, the composition of the team will change as people come and go, and thus there is a measure of control in the medium term. Healthcare is a hands-on business, so staff costs are a relatively high proportion of the costs of running the practice and it is important to staff the practice cost-effectively.

Discretionary expenditure

The areas of expenditure in which yes/no decisions can be made are remarkably few in number. Examples are:
- locums and other temporary staff
- capital expenditure on new or replacement equipment
- maintenance of the premises, particularly redecoration
- training, particularly external courses.

produce a **realistic** **budget** to provide a **rolling** **programme** of **investment**

Sadly, apart from in GP locums, many partnerships are reluctant to invest, particularly in new or replacement equipment, or in staff training. A good finance team will produce a realistic budget to provide a rolling programme of investment in such areas.

Managing expenditure

Once the income of the practice is known, expenditure must be controlled in order to generate a suitable profit. If a sensible programme of investment in the practice is to be maintained (discretionary expenditure), then control must be achieved by managing staff costs. This cannot be done on a day-to-day basis. The team must be able to look ahead and anticipate what will be a sensible level of expenditure on staff in, say, 12 months time.

key to **financial success:** take a **medium-term** view and manage **staff costs**

Searching for a better deal on paper couch rolls actually makes little difference to the big picture. Taking a medium-term view and managing staff costs is the key to financial success.

Profit

Profit is what the partners divide up between them in partnership shares. One of the aims of the nGMS contract was to increase GPs' pay. For partners, that means increasing profit.

As outlined earlier, it is the new money introduced with the QOF which, if managed prudently, should generate an increase in profit. However, once the QOF has become established and the practice is achieving as many points as it realistically can, then no further increase in profit will be achieved in this way. (Remember that new savings from PBC cannot be ploughed into profit.) The new profit level for the practice will depend largely upon how much of the new QOF money has been invested in new or improved services, and thus increased staff costs.

If the government achieves its aim of clawing back what it perceived as over performance by practices in 2004–06, those years may actually represent a peak of practice profits, with profits either being increasingly difficult to sustain, or actually falling, in later years.

Cash flow

The fact that the money obtained by achieving QOF indicators is not determined or paid until after the end of the financial year has major implications. A medium-sized practice earning 990 QOF points will be expecting a final QOF achievement payment of the order of £60 000–80 000. If the practice has decided to invest some of that anticipated income (e.g. in new staff or increased drawings for the partners), which is not unreasonable, then the cost will have to be borne up to 1 full year ahead of receiving the money. As a consequence, many

> money obtained by achieving QOF indicators is not paid until after the end of the financial year

practices may need to borrow significant sums in the later months of the financial year.

Superannuation

Superannuation is a big complication (www.nhspa.gov.uk). One key outcome of the nGMS contract was that, in broad terms, all of a GP's NHS income would be superannuable. These days, partners may be part-time, may work elsewhere (e.g. as a clinical assistant, GP with special interests or a locum) and do sessions for the local out-of-hours service.

The accountants draw together all of a GP's income, determine what superannuation has already been deducted, and provide an end-of-year certificate from which a reconciliation must take place. If insufficient superannuation has been paid on account, the partner is personally liable for the shortfall in the employee's element and the partnership as a whole for the employer's contribution. In 2004–05, payments were largely rolled forward based on the earnings in the previous year, which may not have been enough in many cases. However, after 2005–06, the system should settle into this new way of working.

An additional complication is that, for salaried GPs, superannuation is now deducted from budgets at source. This requires another reconciliation exercise at the end of each financial year for these GPs, depending on their gross pensionable income.

The introduction of the new NHS pension scheme from 2008 will add further complications:

- staff may be members of the old or the new scheme
- employee contribution rates will be tiered, based on gross full-time equivalent salary, or profit, and ranging between 5% and 8.5%.

Tax

Profit is taxable. Some practices pay tax from the partnership account on behalf of the individual partners and thus pay net drawings, and others pay drawings gross and leave it to the individual partner to save enough for the 6-monthly tax bill. With an increase in profit in many practices in the first 1–2 years of the new contract, a consequence was bigger tax bills.

But with profits under attack from 2006 onwards, those tax bills may have to be paid later out of a dwindling income. If tax is paid from the partnership bank account, the finance team will need to make sure that sufficient funds are kept in reserve to meet the demands.

profit is taxable

The PCO finance team

As always, it is not what you know, but who you know. It is important to get to know the key players in the PCO finance team. In particular, identify those who really make the decisions and work through them whenever possible.

Be polite, but tough if necessary. Many PCO finance teams are relatively inexperienced and the days of the finance guru are largely gone. Bids or claims should be presented in a clear, logical way and the case argued step by step. Similar diligence is required when reviewing any budget spreadsheets produced by the PCO, because mistakes are made, which must be found and challenged.

The PCO is the guardian of public funds, but it also has a contractual obligation to pay a practice the fees and allowances to which it is entitled. The practice now has a contract directly with the PCO, whether for GMS or PMS. The PCO must be held to that contract and, if it is in breach of the contract and will not listen to reason, the mechanisms available must be used to bring it to account. If the practice is being denied legitimate funding, dispute proceedings or legal action through the courts (if the practice has opted to be a non-NHS body) should be commenced.

Payroll and drawings

An important administrative task is paying staff and partners at the agreed intervals, usually monthly. Good payroll software is available on the open market, such as Ferguson (www.gppayroll.co.uk) and Sage (www.sage.co.uk). It is important that whoever does the payroll does it well, paying meticulous attention to items such as statutory maternity pay, because there is nothing that annoys staff more than too little pay. It is also important to ensure that the partners' drawings are paid on time, because they have mortgages to service and bills to pay, just like other staff members.

Paying bills

Apart from processing payroll and drawings, practices also tend to have a large number of contractors and suppliers with whom they do business. Apart from the drugs bill in a dispensing practice, the individual payments are often not all that large. The use of systems such as BACS is useful for regular payments and cheques for the rest, though these days a practice debit or credit card is useful, especially for buying over the internet.

The partners should give the finance or practice manager authority to sign cheques up to an agreed limit. This will mean that the day-to-day administration of payments need not result in a chase round the practice trying to find partners to sign cheques. By all means, audit payments made this way to guard against fraud.

Keeping the books

A computerized accounts system is essential. The Maclean McNicoll accounts package (www.gpacc.co.uk, but now part of IRIS software) is a tailored accounts program that is now virtually the industry standard. In business terms, maintaining the accounts of a general practice is relatively straightforward and can largely be done on a cashbook basis. The key is attaching appropriate labels to items of income and expenditure, so that they can be attributed under appropriate headings, and thus aid analysis. A meticulous approach is, however, essential; items should be recorded as they occur and bank statements should be reconciled regularly. Then your end of year should be a relatively painless process.

It should be remembered that it is not only the finance team who needs to understand the accounts; the accountants do as well. For anything unusual, a note should be added in some form so you can answer any queries that the accountant has 18 months later.

Further reading and references

Practice-based commissioning: search www.dh.gov.uk for current guidance.

Statement of Financial Entitlement: search www.dh.gov.uk for GMS Statement of Financial Entitlements

Superannuation: www.nhspa.gov.uk

Ferguson (payroll software): www.gppayroll.co.uk

Sage (payroll software): www.sage.co.uk

Maclean McNicoll accounts package: www.gpacc.co.uk

premises

Barry Coward

A consequence of the independent contractor status of partners in general practice is that most of the premises used to provide NHS services to patients are privately owned. This has led to a financial structure in which the NHS essentially says to the partners 'If you will be kind enough to find premises to provide services to patients registered with the NHS, then we will reimburse you for the costs of providing the building'. The exceptions to this are health centres owned by PCOs.

The majority of premises are thus usually either owned or leased by the partners. If the premises are owned, the financial reimbursement is based on a 'notional' rent, which then goes to service a mortgage. If the premises are leased, a rent agreed by the district valuer will be reimbursed to the practice, which will then pass it on to the landlord. (There is also a cost rent scheme; however, this is too complex to discuss here.)

These arrangements will normally be subject to a 3-yearly rent review, but otherwise are unlikely to change much unless the practice moves to new premises, undergoes major refurbishment or builds an extension.

Existing premises

Premises in which care is taken over facilities, furnishings, decoration, cleaning and maintenance reflect on the practice as a whole. They provide a pleasant environment in which to work, and a comforting and comfortable atmosphere for patients. In contrast, premises that are tatty, tired, badly maintained and dirty should not be tolerated. It cannot be stressed strongly enough that depressing premises make for depressed people. Also, an obvious demarcation between what the partners have and the facilities provided for other GPs and staff does not engender staff morale. Making staff work at non-ergonomic computer workstations and sit on cheap chairs is not only bad in terms of health and safety, but ultimately causes a lot of resentment; it is cheaper to buy a decent chair than recruit and train a new member of staff.

The building needs to function. This means that facilities are maintained and, when something breaks, it is mended – promptly. Skimping on maintenance and decorating is an easy way of saving money in the short term, but often leads to greater costs in the medium term. Keeping the building and its systems up to scratch requires financial investment. It is, however, all too easy to defer such investment as a way of maintaining or increasing the partners' profit share. Furthermore, partners approaching retirement will often oppose a big financial outlay on premises, because it will affect the amount they can take out of the practice on retirement. Therefore, it is far better to establish a rolling programme of investment in the premises that becomes an integral and accepted part of the annual budget.

> **well-cared-for premises** reflect on the **practice** **as a whole**

To maintain the premises, the practice management team needs to:

- have a regular programme of inspections and maintenance, using appropriate contractors (e.g. for the fire alarm system, boilers and portable electrical equipment) as necessary
- keep the building clean
- note and tackle defects promptly.

Inspection and maintenance

All the systems in the practice should be supported by maintenance contracts and should be regularly serviced. This is also now a QOF target.

Maintenance includes redecoration. In a modern building, this may just mean refreshing the paintwork, while in others, a new colour scheme, carefully chosen, can work wonders.

Cleaning

Cleaning is often a headache, whether the practice employs its own cleaners as practice staff or contracts the work out. Either way,

premises

maintaining standards is the most difficult factor in an area of employment where staff turnover is often high.

And when should the cleaning be done? It is difficult to do while patients are being seen, which means cleaners are often in the building either in the early morning or early evening. As a result, they will probably need to hold keys, which have implications for security.

Defects

Most practice managers have a tool kit, and will tighten a screw here and change a light bulb there. Nevertheless, for reasons of health and safety and of employee liability, qualified contractors should be employed for any jobs other than the most minor. A list of good and reliable contractors who can be called on when required must be drawn up.

> draw up a list of good, reliable contractors

New premises

Recently, many new premises have been funded through commercial project management companies, who finance the whole building project in return for a guaranteed rental income at the end – private finance initiative projects in all but name. This concept has now been broadened into the NHS Local Improvement Finance Trust (LIFT) scheme (www.nhsestates.gov.uk).

NHS LIFT scheme

The NHS LIFT approach involves the local health community in developing a strategic service development plan, incorporating local primary care service needs and relationships with, for example, intermediate care and local authority services. A private sector partner will be identified through competitive procurement and a joint venture established between:

- the local health bodies
- Partnerships for Health
- the private sector partner.

The joint venture – the local LIFT company – will have a long-term partnership agreement to deliver investment and services in local care facilities.

New building project

This is an enormous undertaking that will challenge any practice management team. While the detailed management of such a project is beyond the scope of this book, some general advice can be given.

- The project has to be approved as part of the PCO's overall strategy for premises in its area, and funding must be agreed in principle. At the time of writing, funding is managed by a lead PCO in each area, but this may change with time.
- Talk to other practices who have developed new premises recently and learn from their experiences.
- Work closely with the expert on premises in your PCO.
- Read all the guidance that is available; Primary Care Contracting produce some useful information (www.primarycare contracting.nhs.uk/planning-and-design-guidance.php).
- Decide who is going to manage the project within your team and give that person the authority. By all means, consult widely (and wisely), but do not try to run the project by committee. Also, ensure that the person managing the project has the necessary resources, particularly time – employ a temporary assistant if need be.
- Appoint a good solicitor.
- Research all the companies who are involved in LIFT or non-LIFT development of healthcare premises before choosing which one to work with.
- Work with the schedules for the size of building and recommended room sizes to develop an outline design that will work for your practice. Work closely with the architect on the detailed design. The practice is likely to be in this building for 30 years and it is important to get it right.
- Ensure adequate car parking space will be available (see below).
- Involve other members of staff. Seek their views on the rooms in which they will work. Let them feed ideas into the decision-making process, as it will give them a degree of ownership.

- The details are important; for example, getting power points and light switches in the right places makes all the difference.
- Brighten the place up; think about colours, pictures, curtains and furniture.

talk to **other practices** who have **developed new premises**

Major refurbishment or extension?

The considerations are much the same as those for new premises, except on a smaller scale.

Temporary premises

Any new build or major refurbishment on an existing site is likely to entail a move to temporary premises. Very good modular buildings can be hired, with an internal layout to suit different purposes. The main issues to be addressed are:
- finding a suitable temporary location (which will require planning consent)
- laying on mains services (electricity, telephone, water and drains).

The availability of services will often influence the feasibility of any particular site.

Car parking

If there is one common fault with many general practices (and hospitals), it is insufficient car parking space. This inadequacy is often exacerbated by restrictive local planning policies.

Too many practice managers are forced to spend too much time sorting out car parking issues. Many patients see it as their right to park at the practice and will not accept that the car park may be full. Furthermore, if a practice is near a town centre, patients often leave their cars in the car park and go shopping after seeing the doctor!

It is a problem that affects many practices, and there is no easy solution if the space is just not available.

Health and safety

> engender a **culture** **responsive** to **health** **and safety** matters

The management team should engender a culture that is responsive to health and safety matters. The website of the Health and Safety Executive provides an outline of the law (www.hse.gov.uk).

Risk assessment

A formal risk assessment of the workplace should be carried out and documented covering:

- the physical characteristics of the workplace
- first aid provision and facilities
- arrangements for the maintenance and servicing of equipment
- fire risk
- arrangements for visitors
- procedures for the storage, use and disposal of hazardous substances; under the Control of Substances Hazardous to Health Regulations (COSHH), a risk assessment must be carried out at least every 5 years.

Health and safety policy

A practice health and safety policy should be produced that includes:

- a general statement about health and safety policy
- the names of the individuals responsible for that policy
- if applicable, details about the safety committee
- the safety rules
- fire regulations, drills and emergency procedures.

Most features of a health and safety policy are a combination of common sense and good practice (Table 5), though the requirements relating to infection control are of particular importance.

Once a health and safety review has been completed, and a policy written and implemented, it only needs occasional review. All new staff should read the policy document as part of their induction and receive training in the key requirements.

Table 5

Main areas health and safety policy must cover

Fire precautions
- Fire risk assessment
- Fire alarms
- Evacuation procedures
- Fire extinguishers
- Signage

Sharps
- Availability of proper sharps boxes in all consulting and treatment rooms
- Routine for exchanging full boxes
- Safe storage of sharps boxes (particularly away from children)
- Procedure in case of needle-stick injury

Clinical waste
- Proper containers in all consulting and treatment rooms, and in nappy-changing rooms
- Routine for changing full bags
- Locked yellow skip

Bodily fluids
- Routine for dealing with spillage of bodily fluids
- Protective clothing
- Clean-up kits

Mercury spillage
- Policy on mercury sphygmomanometers
- Routine for dealing with spillage
- Clean-up kit

Sterilization of instruments
- Routine for sterilization of instruments or contract for the job
- Maintenance and testing of in-house sterilizing equipment
- Records

Drugs

- Security of controlled drugs
- Security of non-controlled drugs
- Authority to dispense or administer drugs
- Temperature control of vaccines

Hazardous substances in treatment room

- COSHH risk assessment
- Risk reduction
- Safety and handling procedures

Oxygen

- Storage
- Safety procedures
- Warning notices

Protective clothing

- Tabards or aprons
- Gloves
- Eye protection
- Ear defenders
- Footwear
- Overalls

First aid

- First-aid kits
- Staff trained in first aid (yes, even in a general practice!)

Power failure

- Procedure in case of power failure
- Restoration drill

Disabled access

- Access routes
- Lift if practice is on more than one floor
- Wheelchair for temporarily disabled patients

Building or system design features
- Fire hazards
- No mixing of water and electricity
- Gas supplies
- Access
- Ventilation
- Heating and cooling
- Lift
- Maintenance
- Procedure in case of lift failure
- Automatic doors
- Safety features
- Regular testing

Electrical
- Loading of power points
- Cable runs
- Circuit breakers
- Extension leads
- Minimize permanent use
- Hazard warning for temporary use

Staffing levels
- Minimum number of staff in the building, with and without patients present

Safety of staff from patient violence
- Panic alarms
- Design of reception desk
- Escape routes
- Chaperoning of patients
- Flagging risk patients
- Security locks
- Keys
- Policy on home visits, particularly by female staff

Systems of work
- Safe working practices
- Work within capability of member of staff
- Sufficient guidance, training and/or supervision
- Rest facilities
- System for dealing with defects or hazards

Stress
- Measures to avoid and reduce stress
- Avoidance of bullying or harassment

Lifting and carrying
- Training
- Procedure for lifting heavy patients
- Provision of aids (e.g. trolleys)

Musculoskeletal injury
- Avoidance of repetitive strain injury
- Workstation ergonomics
- Rest periods
- Methods of working
- Headsets for telephone work
- Chairs
- Footrests

Eyes
- Lighting levels
- Computer screens
- Working conditions
- Eye tests
- Provision of glasses

Toilets
- Provision of toilet paper, soap and towels
- Cleaning

Domestic fridges and microwaves
- Cleaning
- Disposal of out-of-date items

Cleaning materials
- Safety of hazardous cleaning materials
- Disposal

Toys
- Inspection
- Cleaning
- Safety of toys

Access to high places
- Provide kick-steps for staff to reach shelves
- Provide stepladders for maintenance access

Ground maintenance
- Extent of work by own staff
- Risk assessment
- Use of contractors

Slippery surfaces
- Internal during cleaning
- External if icy
- Provision of salt and treatment of paths

Cleaning
- Cleaners/cleaning contracts
- Standards and routines

Tools
- Provide the right tools for the job (e.g. letter openers, staple removers, maintenance tool kit)
- Power tools
- Training
- Authorization to use

Visitors
- Procedures to ensure the safety of visitors

Training
- Training of staff in health and safety measures

Maintenance and testing
- Maintenance and testing of systems and equipment
- Use of contractors where necessary
- Regular inspection of portable electrical equipment

Information and documentation
- Information and procedures for staff
- Maintenance routines
- Test certificates

by example, ensure health and safety policy is implemented day-to-day

Management should set an example and ensure that health and safety policy is implemented on a day-to-day basis through gentle guidance, occasional reminders, and a walk around the building looking for hazards and what is required.

Disability Discrimination Act

The Disability Discrimination Act (www.opsi.gov.uk/acts/acts1995/ukpga_19950050_en_1 and www.direct.gov.uk/en/DisabledPeople) makes it unlawful for a service provider to discriminate against a disabled person by refusing to provide any service that it provides to members of the public. The big change in law came in 2004 when service providers, which include general practices, had to make reasonable adjustments to the physical features of their premises to overcome physical barriers to access.

A person has a disability if he/she has a physical or mental impairment that has a substantial and long-term adverse effect on his/her ability to carry out normal day-to-day activities. Physical or mental impairment includes sensory impairments. Hidden impairments are also covered (e.g. mental illness or mental health problems, learning disabilities and conditions such as diabetes or epilepsy).

In general practice, such people are treated on a daily basis. In order to ensure that they can gain access to the premises and services as freely as possible, the practice has a duty to make reasonable adjustments by:

- changing methods of working, policies and procedures
- providing auxiliary aids and services
- overcoming a physical feature by removing it, altering it, avoiding it or providing services by alternative methods.

While the image of disability tends to centre around the wheelchair and the difficulties of access, it is important to consider the potential issues more widely. This is illustrated by the following examples.

- Disabled parking spaces close to the main entrance are reserved exclusively for orange/blue badge holders, but a driver delivering a patient who cannot walk easily also needs to be able to park in such spaces.
- Some practices use an electronic display to call the next patient, but provision must be made for the blind and those who cannot read.
- If consultations are carried out in a room accessed by stairs that are a rather dull brown colour, measures should be taken to make them easier to pick out by a patient with impaired vision.

do not focus on the **wheelchair** when **considering DDA issues**

Although it should not be necessary to make any major physical changes to modern practice premises, considerable changes may be required to older premises. Another factor to bear in mind is that employers are now required to make reasonable changes to enable a person with a disability to be employed. Cost is one test of reasonableness.

Contingency plans

If your building burned down, could you re-establish the core business within 48 hours? When the IRA bombed buildings in the City of London in the 1980s, some businesses were up and running in alternative locations within 24 hours, while others never recovered and went out of business.

> if your **building burned down,** could you re-establish the **core business** within **48 hours?**

General practices are not major financial institutions whose very existence depends on the continuity of business. However, it is important to have the capability to re-establish essential services to patients quickly, and routine services within a few days. In order to be able to do this quickly and efficiently, back-ups of key data and materials must be held off site, including:

- prescription pads
- computer data, ideally in a form that can be easily loaded straight back onto the computer
- inventory of equipment and furniture, as well as phone numbers of suppliers
- telephone numbers routinely used by the practice
- accounts, payroll and administrative data
- details of staff, including contact numbers
- paper administrative files.

Finally, it is important to ensure that the insurance will cover the full costs of the recovery plan.

Other contingencies for which plans should be drawn up include:

- power cut or planned power outage
- lift failure with people inside
- telephone system failure
- main computer file server failure
- failure of individual PCs
- loss of mains water or blocked drains
- heating system failure
- jammed door locks and safes that will not open
- intruder alarm activation
- loss of important keys.

Further reading and references

NHS Local Improvement Finance Trust (LIFT) scheme: search www.dh.gov.uk for NHS LIFT; www.nhsestates.gov.uk

New buildings: www.primarycarecontracting.nhs.uk/planning-and-design-guidance.php

Health and safety matters: www.hse.gov.uk

Disability Discrimination Act: www.opsi.gov.uk/acts/acts1995/ukpga_19950050_en_1; www.direct.gov.uk/en/DisabledPeople

a service to patients

Sue Gooding
Practice Manager

We now live in an increasingly '24/7' society in which patients' expectations of the health service often do not fit reality and the resources available. This inevitably creates tensions between patients and the practice team. The challenge for the team is to deal with these expectations so that patients feel satisfied that their needs have been met, and not just that they must adapt to the way services are provided. However, general practice does not have infinite funding and can only provide services to the level that resources allow, while ensuring that members of the primary healthcare team (GPs, nurses, and reception and administration staff) are able to achieve a reasonable work–life balance.

> patients' expectations of the **health service** often do not fit **reality**

Factors affecting service delivery

Many external factors affect both the type of service and its delivery to patients, for example:

- government/DoH directives – the NHS Plan
- the national IT project, CfH
- the PCO
- the new GP contract
- the entire Choice agenda.

Most of these factors are outside of the control of the practice team and require the implementation of changes within the practice that may be perceived as 'just more bureaucracy'. However, the way in which these measures are implemented can be controlled.

Nevertheless, most patients have little interest in NHS directives and just want a good, accessible service within a reasonable distance of where they live.

Making change work

A number of interrelated and interdependent factors influence the ability of a practice to offer the best possible service. These include:

- teamwork
- communication
- training
- policies and procedures (systems)
- use of technology – telephones and IT
- premises/environment
- patient involvement.

all members of the team should use the same guidelines and procedures

The overriding factor in providing a good service is good teamwork. This requires all members of the team to work towards a common goal and to use the same guidelines and procedures so that patients experience a consistent, efficient and effective service.

Good communication is, of course, essential for good teamwork. A well-informed team will work well together and support one another in the delivery of an excellent service. Good communication can be established through:

- regular team meetings
- memos
- verbal communication
- newsletters
- email
- website
- periodic practice awaydays.

The methods of communication should be chosen to suit the diversity of the team.

In addition, good systems with written policies and procedures will provide support for the team, and ensure that they are working to an agreed process/standard to provide a consistent and high standard of service. As many of the team members will work part-time, common methods of working are essential if consistency is to be maintained. Wherever possible, systems should be formulated by the team and made available as hard copy or electronically through the practice intranet, so that they are easily accessible to all team members. Written policies and procedures will also be invaluable to new team members.

> **written policies** and **procedures** will provide **support** for the **team**

Reception

The reception staff are very much the 'face and voice' of the practice and their skill in dealing with patients will reflect on the practice as a whole. As the facilitators of patients' access to healthcare, reception staff need to have a friendly, helpful and confident manner, and be competent in their role.

In order to deliver an excellent service to patients, reception staff must be provided with efficient systems, training, and up-to-date and accessible information. Again teamwork is essential, both within the reception team and the wider practice team. The reception staff will implement the systems that have been agreed by the practice, and will need the support of the practice manager and the GPs. If the practice systems are failing to meet patients' needs, it will be the reception staff who will bear the brunt of their dissatisfaction.

Dealing with aggression and violence

Sadly, one essential document concerns the practice and PCO policy on dealing with aggressive and violent patients. The problem of aggression and violence towards professionals and staff within the NHS is increasing, and a service-wide policy of 'zero tolerance' has been adopted.

The risk posed to each practice should be assessed and steps taken to minimize that risk. The practice team should be trained to deal with difficult or aggressive patients, so that they can defuse a potentially dangerous situation and help to ensure the safety of themselves and other patients. Installing a panic alarm system (mechanical or electronic using the telephone or computer systems) throughout the practice may be considered; however, a protocol must be established for responding to the alarm, so that all members are aware of the appropriate action to take, including designated staff going to the scene of the incident and someone bearing responsibility for calling the police if physical violence is involved.

> a service-wide policy of 'zero tolerance' has been adopted

Accessing services

Patients' access to practice services will invariably involve the use of technology. However, the technology should be seen as a tool to enhance patients' access, not something that dictates the process. What suits one patient may not suit another, and it may be necessary to offer a variety of means of access.

A good telephone system with sufficient lines for the volume of calls is essential. Most current systems also have an automated answering system that offers a number of other facilities to improve access. Such systems can:

- redirect patients to the appropriate team member
- advise patients if they are in a call queue
- remind patients of appropriate times to call for information such as results
- allow patients to cancel appointments out of normal surgery hours, reducing 'did not appear' rates
- allow patients to book appointments outside of normal surgery hours.

Such telephone systems can also offer call recording, which can be useful for training and dealing with complaints.

Good use of IT can also improve access by enabling patients to book appointments and order repeat prescriptions over the internet, so that again they can access the surgery when it suits them and not just when it is open. IT can also be used to increase efficiency once the patient arrives at the practice, through the use of touch-screen computers, which enable patients to book themselves in, and electronic display screens to tell patients the doctor is available and to inform them of any delays.

> technology should enhance patients' access, not dictate the process

Access targets

While fostering good teamwork and systems undoubtedly improves patients' access to the service, meeting the access targets may be a greater challenge. The government has used the targets as a way of improving access to appointments. The mechanisms for setting the targets have used a mixture of an Enhanced Service and QOF targets, but the key elements, which have changed and will no doubt change again, include:

- short-term availability of appointments, e.g. 48 hours for a GP (any GP, not a specific GP)
- at the same time, ability to book ahead
- ability to speak to healthcare professionals on the telephone.

Achieving these targets will require periodic review of demand and appointment availability, by measuring demand (counting all requests for appointments for a period of time) and comparing and matching this with the number of appointments available. A flexible appointment schedule that can adjust to changes in demand can help in reaching the target, together with the adoption of the principles of 'advanced access', in other words, dealing with today's work today. This aim requires sufficient appointments to meet the demand on each day.

The Access agenda expanded rapidly in 2007. The results of the first national survey of patients, published in mid-2007, showed generally very high satisfaction (80% plus in many areas) with access, availability of appointments and ability to speak to a GP. Very controversially, the survey also asked questions about opening hours. Again patients expressed very high satisfaction, with only a relatively small minority expressing a desire for extended hours.

However, the government nevertheless chose to put extended opening hours for GP practices high on the political agenda for the NHS. The ideas emerging by the end of 2007 included:

- new resources to enable PCOs to set up 150 GP-run health centres open 7 days a week, 8 am to 8 pm, situated in easily accessible locations and offering a range of services to ensure more patients have access to GP treatment and advice at a time that is convenient to them, including pre-bookable appointments, walk-in services and other services
- at least half of all GP practices opening on Saturday mornings or one or more evenings each week.

In 2008 and beyond, this is likely to be one of the largest issues affecting general practice. The factors affecting a practice's ability to respond include:

- funding
- the working time directive and whether extended hours can be contained within the limits for salaried staff
- whether GPs and staff are actually willing to work extended hours
- childcare constraints and the conflict with family-friendly employment practices
- whether or not patients will actually attend during the extended hours
- the reduction in services that may occur at other times of day if GPs' work is 'spread out' more
- what threats are imposed for non-compliance; what incentives for responding.

Staffing and administration

The staffing structure of a practice will largely depend on its size. A larger practice may have dedicated reception staff, who deal only with telephone and face-to-face enquiries from patients for appointments, and pass all other issues on to other team members. A small practice, on the other hand, may require its reception staff to deal with a variety of tasks.

The service offered by a practice includes a myriad administrative tasks, ranging from informing patients about the results of investigations, follow-up of hospital attendances, routine calls and recalls for chronic disease management and cytology, patient registration, and maintaining patients' records either manually or electronically. Robust, written protocols must be in place to deal with all these tasks and, furthermore, need to be designed in such a way that other team members can pick up and follow the procedures in the absence of key personnel.

> written protocols should be designed so other team members can pick up and follow the procedures

Repeat prescriptions

An efficient repeat prescription service is an important element of the service to patients, as is the dispensing of all prescriptions.

A dispensing practice may have dedicated dispensing staff who deal with all prescription issues. In a practice with a pharmacy within the surgery, all dispensing and related tasks may be subcontracted to the pharmacy.

In a non-dispensing practice, the reception staff will probably administer repeat prescriptions and deal with medication queries. They will need to be given a written procedure outlining how the system works and the timescales involved. This should also be described in the practice leaflet so that patients are fully aware of the system. Non-dispensing practices will also need to foster good relationships with local pharmacists, support their prescription collection service and deal with queries promptly. As far as the patient is concerned, a 'lost' repeat prescription can be a serious problem.

Practice managers must keep abreast of changes, such as the Repeat Dispensing Scheme, which enables repeat prescriptions to be issued in batches, and the Electronic Prescription transfer facility, which is becoming available under the CfH programme.

Further reading and references

The new GMS contract and the NHS Plan: search www.dh.gov.uk for primary care contracting

Connecting for Health (National Programme for IT): www.connectingforhealth.nhs.uk

practice-based commissioning and related changes

Barry Coward

The trials of 2003–04, which involved introducing the new GMS contract, learning to work with the QOF and Enhanced Services, and implementing radically different financial structures, were cast aside in early 2005. Management teams hardly had time to catch their breath before the next wave of new initiatives came sweeping over the horizon:

- PBC
- Choose and Book
- Payment by Results.

The reaction of most teams was one of chronic change fatigue.

Practice-based commissioning

The PBC framework, which was originally published in early 2005, was left very broadly defined. Since then, the guidance has been expanded and refined, but still leaves room for some flexibility and initiative. However, interference by the government appeared to be increasing, so that a concept which was broadly worded when first mooted looked as if it would be closely managed in detail from the centre. However, as PBC has matured, PCOs and practices have largely been left to get on with it.

The original underlying thinking was that GPs engender a great deal of the activity in the secondary and community sectors by referring patients for further care, but had little awareness of how much that process cost. Thus, it was thought that if those who refer patients were given some incentive, then the process could be better managed and costs could be reduced.

However, it is not just about costs. It also blurs the edges of the 'traditional' split between primary and secondary care, and offers patients treatment nearer to home, which many would perceive as an improvement in the service. Such a service could be provided by:

- healthcare professionals with specialist interests serving groups of practices
- local treatment centres
- provision of more care within the practice setting
- commissioning services from 'willing providers', who may be members of the NHS 'family' or could be private organizations.

A combination of all four could also be employed.

Thus, the core concept of PBC is that practices help to shape and commission services to meet local needs.

> through **PBC,** practices help **shape** and **commission** services to **meet local needs**

Choose and Book

Choose and Book falls within the broader 'choice' agenda, and is designed to expand patients' choice as to where they receive secondary care. From a choice of a limited range of treatments and providers at the beginning, the concept remains that Choose and Book will expand to cover most treatments provided almost anywhere in the country.

Choose and Book can only succeed if first-class information is available to assist patients in making a choice. The IT system behind it has now developed to the stage where:

- a directory of services can be searched online and a choice of secondary care providers offered to patients
- most referral letters and supporting results can be passed to secondary care providers electronically
- a means of booking an appointment can be offered at the time of referral, either through direct booking or indirect booking (where the patient has to telephone to make the appointment themselves).

practice-based commissioning and related changes

Choose and Book can be said to stand in contrast to PBC. The latter is largely about improving local services, working with local hospitals to improve patient care pathways, and bringing care closer to the patient. Choose and Book theoretically offers the patient the opportunity to go wherever they like for care. But what has emerged is that most patients do not want choice; they want first-class services at their local hospital. Thus Choose and Book is rapidly developing simply into a system that allows electronic referrals to a local hospital. In some areas, there will be genuine choice for patients across a handful of local hospitals, but that is as far as the vast majority of patients wish it to go.

Payment by Results

The concept behind Payment by Results is very simple – care providers, principally secondary care providers, should be paid for each episode of care provided (see page 26). This is in place of 'block' contracts for which hospitals were paid a fixed amount, whatever the activity levels.

> PbR shifts **financial risk** from **hospitals** to PCOs

Although simple in theory, paying for each episode of care introduces many complications, including the financial accounting infrastructure to manage the process. And block contracts were never that simple either.

One very important feature of Payment by Results is that the tariffs are fixed. There is no opportunity within the structure to negotiate on price. As a result, the financial risk shifts significantly from the hospitals to the PCOs. If the hospitals do more work, they get more money. However, that money comes from a fixed pot held by the PCOs.

The new environment

The new GMS contract brought in major changes in 2004:
- an enormous incentive to improve the quality of care (QOF)
- an opportunity to decline some areas of work and take on others (Enhanced Services)
- cessation of the out-of-hours commitment.

PBC, Choose and Book and Payment by Results appeared on the primary care agenda early in 2005, changing the primary care environment still further. However PBC, CAB and PbR were not only the abbreviations of the day, but also heralded a more subtle change in the primary care environment. Implicitly, the 'right' of general practices to be the providers of primary care services is no longer fully protected. Indeed, many recent developments have already widened the scope of primary care. Community nursing and health visiting teams have long been part of the primary care spectrum, but developments in the early 2000s have led to a much broader picture, which includes:

- community hospitals (not new)
- NHS Direct
- out-of-hours services
- in-hours services such as local minor injuries units
- walk-in centres
- pharmacists, whose role is developing under the 2005 pharmacy contract
- and, most importantly, mechanisms that allow private providers to bid for primary care services.

The subtle change that PBC, CAB and PbR introduce to the primary care environment is that PCOs will be looking ever more closely at cost-effectiveness. Practices that are expensive users of NHS services will fall under the spotlight. At the same time, strong practice-based commissioners have the opportunity to drive the local agenda and to work with PCOs in developing local strategies. Choose and Book and Payment by Results are tools; PBC is what counts.

strong practice-based commissioners can drive the local agenda

For many years now, practices' prescribing spends have been under close scrutiny. Detailed information on spend and prescribing patterns is now the norm. Incentive schemes are devised by PCOs to encourage savings; comparative data are published to encourage high spenders to fall in line with their peers.

Similar developments can now be expected in the field of commissioning. Practices, implicitly, will have to demonstrate value for money, not only in the provision of primary care services, but also in their

practice-based commissioning and related changes

use of secondary services. Practices that choose not to embrace the new agenda may ultimately not survive in their current form.

Role of the practice management team

The reality is that PBC got off to a very slow start in many parts of the country and will continue to evolve over many years. It will also emerge in different forms in different areas; inner-city commissioning will be different from that in rural areas. However, all practice management teams must address six essential areas:

- management of referrals
- development of alternative care pathways
- business-like approach
- information management
- funding of clinical and management time
- management of freed-up resources.

In the same way that GPs have had different prescribing patterns, they also have different referral patterns. Referral patterns are influenced by many factors, including:

- a GP's experience, or lack of it
- confidence
- whether or not the GP has previously had some training in a particular specialization
- whether the GP is a permanent member of the practice or a locum
- an adverse experience in the past (e.g. a complaint), which has made a GP tend to refer earlier in particular circumstances
- the likelihood or otherwise of a referral being accepted by a given provider
- the availability of a particular service or category of care
- patient pressure.

The practice management team will need to engender an atmosphere in which referral patterns can be discussed among team members in a positive, constructive way and, where appropriate, modified over time.

developing **alternative care pathways** goes **hand-in-hand** with a **business-like approach**

The development of alternative care pathways goes hand-in-hand with a business-like approach. The thrust will be to examine ways in which care might be provided:

- locally
- ideally in the primary care setting
- more cheaply
- quickly.

If an area of work is going to be brought back into the primary care setting, someone has to do that work, whether it is a GP or a nurse. And if they are doing that work, they cannot do all the other everyday work. Set up a nurse-led clinic for an afternoon a week to take on some specialist work, and the hours 'lost' from other work must be filled.

It is implicit that if work is to move more towards the primary care setting, then people are going to have to move as well – away from hospitals. If primary care is to be a cheaper provider of care, then either the costs of staff in primary care are lower than in hospitals (a dubious assumption, particularly in the era of Agenda for Change) or the overheads of providing a service in primary care are lower.

Balanced against this are economies of scale. Having doctors or nurses trained in specialist roles is only cost-effective if they can use those skills effectively. Sending a nurse on a course costing several thousand pounds is hardly justified if only one patient a week is treated as a result.

> management of **PBC** requires good information

The management of PBC requires good information. Thus, a major part of the development of PBC has involved data gathering and improving the coverage, quality and timeliness of such data. The major lesson emerging in the early stages was that the data with which PCOs and practices had to work needed significant improvement in accuracy and timeliness.

Working with other practices has become important. Indeed, locality commissioning is seen as a key element of PBC and has led to the emergence of locality commissioning management structures.

None of this can be achieved without the management resources to undertake the work or the funding to support those resources. Management teams were hard pressed in 2003–04 to bring in the new contract, but at least there were positive financial incentives to encourage achievement, principally through the QOF. The incentives built into PBC have not been nearly so encouraging; indeed, it is implicit in the whole idea that GPs, nurses and managers have an altruistic desire to improve things, and will thus undertake the extra work involved without additional reward to themselves.

Practice-based commissioning, Choose And Book and Payment by Results will all mature over several years. They may or may not turn out to be the salvation of the NHS and primary care. But whichever way things develop, these concepts will tax practice management teams over the next few years.

Funding of clinical and management time

PBC, if done at all, takes a lot of clinical and management time. A model which has evolved in many areas is that of the local PBC consortia being run by some form of executive or management committee, possibly employing a small number of dedicated staff, and with individual GPs, managers or practices taking the lead on specific topics. This means that GPs and managers are spending time both doing work on PBC within their own practices and attending PBC meetings.

The funding provided for this work, through a DES to start with and then evolving into a PCO incentive or similar scheme, is in itself inadequate. The lack of resources to support the work required has been one of the key factors leading to the very slow development of PBC.

Freed-up resources

One of the principles of PBC is that savings made can be re-invested, and that practices should have a say in how up to 70% of those savings are used. It was only after the end of 2006/07 that the reality of managing freed-up resources started to become apparent. Issues arise over how much control lies with individual practices over the savings they make against pooling savings to achieve consortia-wide improvements.

PCOs have allowed freed-up resources to be spent not only on service improvements but also equipment buys, building projects, staff training, etc. In fact the nature of freed-up resources, being non-recurring, has meant that investment in medium-term service improvements is difficult because there is no guarantee that funding can be sustained. Thus, spending of freed-up resources on service improvements tends to be limited to one-off projects or pump-priming a new service before sustainable funding becomes available.

Further reading and references

Practice-based commissioning: search www.dh.gov.uk for current guidance

Choose and Book: www.chooseandbook.nhs.uk

Payment by Results: search www.dh.gov.uk for current guidance

practice-based commissioning and related changes

working with partners

Barry Coward

Doctors, particularly older doctors, have been trained in the ethos of the independent practitioner, making decisions alone about patients under their care. Such doctors are therefore, by their nature, not natural team players but can, nevertheless, find themselves thrust into partnerships in general practice.

A partnership is like a marriage, though without the sex; and like marriages, quite a lot, sadly, end in a split. No practice functions effectively unless the partnership works. The management of the partnership is, therefore, a key function of the practice management team. But, of course, the partners are themselves part of that management team.

So what is the role of the partners in managing the practice?

- They own the practice in terms of its assets, which may include the premises or the right to a tenancy of the premises, the furniture and equipment, and drug stocks.

> a partnership is like a marriage ...

- They employ the practice staff.
- They are the equivalent of the Board of a company.
- They have a real stake in the practice, in that they have invested their own money in the practice, and their income is dependent on a share of the practice profits.
- They decide the strategy for the future of the practice.

Much has been written about being a partner in general practice, so this chapter aims to consider the problem of how to manage the partners themselves in exercising their role as 'the Board'.

The partnership secretary

It is appropriate to appoint a partnership secretary, who will have responsibility for (among other things) carrying out the administrative work of the partnership, calling partnership meetings, organizing the agenda and drafting the minutes. The partnership secretary will often, but not necessarily, be the practice manager.

The partnership agreement

partnerships without **formal agreements** are founded on **legal quicksand**

The partnership agreement is an important legal document; a solicitor's advice should be sought on the drafting. Partnerships without formal agreements are founded on legal quicksand.

From the management point of view, two elements of the partnership agreement have an important impact on the way business is run:

- how partnership decisions are made
- how the money is shared out among the partners.

Decision-making

Much of the decision-making in a partnership is based on consensus. A discussion will lead to a view with which no partner fundamentally disagrees, and therefore a decision is made. It is extremely rare for matters to be put to a vote. A partnership that has to vote formally on everything is probably a partnership in trouble. At the same time, partnerships that depend on unanimous agreement on everything are unlikely to make much progress. For everyday matters, a simple one-partner, one-vote system will get business done and, if no consensus is reached, the majority view will prevail.

It may be better to take major decisions (e.g. taking on a new partner) using a majority-weighted voting system, based on partnership shares and agreement that a certain percentage of the weighted vote must be in favour for a decision to be made. However, what constitutes 'major decisions' must be defined in the partnership agreement.

It is also important that a quorum is defined, so that no partner can prevent decisions being made simply by failing to attend, particularly if it has reached the stage where the expulsion of that absent partner is being decided!

Money

The financial aspect of the partnership agreement needs to be drawn up carefully so that the finance team can allot each partner suitable drawings on a day-by-day basis. The practice accountants will also need to know the details so they can allot profit shares appropriately in the practice accounts.

While percentage profit shares should be easy to agree, other aspects to be defined include:

- whether the partners' tax liability is paid personally or through the practice account
- whether medical defence union fees are a personal or practice expense
- whether General Medical Council (GMC) registration and British Medical Association (BMA) membership are a personal or practice expense
- how private fees earned by the partners and paid into the practice are treated.

Managing the partners

Regular partnership meetings are important, and should be scheduled as protected time. The partnership secretary should draw up an agenda, which will almost certainly include business that needs to be conducted with the partners. Some of that business may simply consist of bringing the partners up to date on certain matters or just seeking their views.

prepare and **circulate** a **briefing paper before** the **partnership meetings**

A report on the current financial outlook is a standard item on most partnership meeting agendas.

A helpful way to get business transacted efficiently is for the partnership secretary to prepare and circulate a briefing paper before the meeting.

The minutes of partnership meetings need not cover every facet of the discussion but should, at the very least, record the decisions. However, it is difficult to trawl through the minutes to check what was decided about a particular issue in the past, so it is useful to keep a separate list of the key decisions made over the lifetime of the partnership.

Lead partners

In any partnership, but certainly in larger partnerships, it is useful to have partners who lead in certain areas (e.g. finance, staff, contracts, IT). The practice manager can then direct appropriate day-to-day business to that partner. Otherwise the danger is that business will stall waiting for the next partners' meeting. While the lead partners should be given authority to make day-to-day decisions within their areas, they should also keep the other partners informed.

Day-to-day business

Apart from having lead partners, it is important that authority and responsibility are delegated to the managers employed by the practice. There are few things more frustrating for the practice manager, for example, than the lack of authority to make decisions and get things done. A good management team with delegated authority will get on with the running of the practice and use partners' meetings to reach an understanding of the strategic direction.

use **partners' meetings** to reach an **understanding** of the **strategic direction**

From time to time, decisions may be required quickly, and the practice manager may have to sound out the partners' views. If the practice has a schedule of regular practice meetings (e.g. critical incident meetings, clinical governance meetings), then an additional 10-minute discussion at the end of such a session can get a decision that allows business to move forward.

The reality

Partners are busy people, but they do own the practice and have a financial stake in it. The management team will need to ascertain the partners' wishes from time to time, and that process can be assisted by providing information in advance and steering matters towards a decision. Although partners do have different styles of working, progress can be achieved if these are recognized and acknowledged, but not allowed to inhibit activity.

An overbearing and dominant partner can, on the other hand, be very difficult to deal with. One advantage of PMS practices, which also now applies to GMS, is that any GP can be taken on in a salaried status initially. This allows a period of mutual assessment before a partnership is offered. Any partnership would also do well to listen to the views of the partnership secretary and/or practice manager before agreeing to take on a new partner, because they will have seen this person from a different point of view.

Finally, despite the advantages of having lead partners, it is wise to structure matters such that a single partner does not have authority to act unilaterally in any area that could get the partnership into difficulties. This can be vital in terms of issues concerning employment law, where one rash decision by a partner (e.g. to dismiss an employee instantly) can plunge the partnership into deep water. A clause in the partnership agreement placing liability in such circumstances entirely on that partner who acted unilaterally works wonders.

working with staff

Jenny Stenhouse
Trainer

'Give us the tools and we will finish the job.'
Winston Churchill, 1941

Without the tools of management, the practice team will not function efficiently and effectively, the practice will not be a happy one and the patients will suffer.

The principles of managing staff in a practice are similar to those in commerce and industry. However, patience is another dimension to add to the list of desirable qualities of leadership and administration. Communication and empathy at the highest level are necessary to enhance the outcomes of the managerial role.

The question is, are these characteristics in place to ensure the maintenance and development of a happy and united team?

- Are staff motivated?
- Is there a visible training plan?
- Is input from everyone encouraged?
- Are there opportunities for tasks and authority to be delegated?
- Is there a recognized action plan for discipline?
- Is teamwork recognized as a priority?
- Is constructive criticism given and received?
- Are rewards given?
- Are staff skills utilized appropriately?

Motivation

motivation is about **exciting to action**

Motivation is about inducement, exciting to action, giving incentives and impetus – but how is this done? Certainly there is a limit on money as a motivator. However, the practice management team can create the right conditions for staff to be motivated more effectively.

- Offer training.
- Concentrate on strengths.
- Implement job rotation.
- Involve staff in decision-making.
- Increase responsibility.
- Appraise.
- Identify personal goals.
- Ensure that a clear career structure is in place.
- Reward staff, and show that you care.

Training

> 'Whenever you have been involved in changing behaviour, you have been a trainer.'
> P Hackett in *Introduction to Training*

Training within a practice happens at many levels, not least on a day-to-day basis between colleagues. However, a formal plan that recognizes staff needs while reflecting the practice's aims and priorities is essential for motivation and team building. The key aspects of training are to:

- meet the needs of the staff, as identified by appraisal and discussion
- reflect the aims, goals and priorities of the practice
- ensure that finance and time are available
- check that the training is appropriate and relates to needs
- make time for feedback.

Success will come only if the trainee's effort is concentrated and focused, and that effort is valued. One-off events, without feedback and evaluation, are a waste of money and time. The types of training that should be considered are summarized in Table 6 (page 110).

Although external training budgets are no longer imposed, practices must remain clearly motivated to develop their staff, and so must maintain a training culture. The benefits of training for the practice include:

- greater job satisfaction and thus a lower staff turnover
- a higher standard of service, leading to an enhanced practice profile
- greater patient satisfaction
- increase in income when targets are met.

Personal development plans provide motivation for individuals. In addition, effective training leads to better job satisfaction, promotion prospects and skill transferability.

> **effective training** leads to **better job satisfaction**

Staff rotation

Going round in circles may be an example of having a bad day, but it may also be a good policy to prevent staff boredom! The advantages of job rotation are as follows.

- Nobody spends too long on one task, losing motivation.
- Boredom is avoided while quality is ensured.
- Everyone gains experience in everything, so that staff absences cause fewer problems.
- The least favourite tasks are shared.
- An individual cannot 'hog' the most pleasant role.

Within job rotation it is still possible to recognize specific skills and to have a lead person in certain areas.

To ensure recognized standards within each role, it is essential for staff to have adequate training as well as written guidance for every aspect of administrative work in the practice. This guidance need not be exhaustive, but a written sheet, kept in a recognized folder, helps both new and experienced staff to deal with any aspect of their work. The other advantage of written guidance is the prevention of the 'sitting by Nellie' approach to training, whereby incorrect information is passed on from colleague to colleague.

Table 6

Advantages and disadvantages of different types of training

Type of training	Advantages	Disadvantages
In-house, using members of the team	Inexpensive Familiarity with the surroundings leads to a tailor-made approach Use of time maximized	May not be structured May not be evaluated Not always valued by recipients
In-house, using an outside trainer	Less expensive than sending everyone out Use of time maximized New face respected and valued Recognized expertise	Trainer may not be familiar with the practice and individual needs and priorities
At a local college, with a generic trainer	Meeting other people in a similar role, comparing and sharing procedures Staff feel valued by having dedicated time Recognized expertise	Not tailored to the needs of the individual One-off event, with no lasting application May be broad-based, without knowledge of the needs of general practice
At another practice or chosen venue, with a specialist trainer	Ideal for sharing experiences Participants feel less threatened by a familiar venue, and will join in more freely Trainer has knowledge of the organization	May be seen by participants as an opportunity to chat with others in the same role, without constructive sharing Venue may be unsuitable for training

Holiday rotas

Holidays are fun for those taking them, but hard work for those left behind. Dealing with requests for leave is a thorn in the side of many a manager, and getting it wrong can have disastrous effects.

A firm policy must be in place and must be adhered to, because everyone will feel at some time that they are a special case. School holidays and partners or spouses who have set holidays are probably the major sources of dissension in a team.

> create and **adhere** to a **firm** policy on **leave**

Factors to consider

- Is a practice policy in place and is this written into staff contracts (e.g. no more than two members away at any one time, no Christmas leave)?
- Does the policy recognize flexible working hours at certain potentially busy times (e.g. Christmas)?
- Have you confirmed each staff member's holiday allowance with them?
- Have you the means to use temporary staff?
- When new staff are employed, are they told about the need to provide cover?
- Do you discuss with all staff what their needs are and how the practice will cope (i.e. do you involve everyone in decision-making)?

Getting it right is important for the practice and for the individuals concerned, but you have to keep to the rules. Getting it wrong leads to dissatisfaction, unhappy staff and a lowering of standards.

Keeping everyone happy

Conflict at work causes serious problems and can have a disastrous effect on team morale. A recent survey found that many managers and supervisors spend up to 25% of

> it is **better** to **prevent conflict** than to have to **manage** it

their working time attempting to resolve conflicts. Handling conflict well is of benefit to the practice, but it is still better to recognize the causes of conflict and manage them constructively to prevent it.

Methods of preventing conflict

- Hold regular staff meetings.
- Consult staff, especially if a decision affects them.
- Counsel staff who may be the cause of a problem.
- Do not discuss individuals with other staff members.
- Keep contracts and job descriptions up to date.
- Praise and reward.
- Have a grievance procedure in place.
- Face conflict; don't ignore it.

In summary, trained and motivated staff who are managed well will provide a service that we would like to receive as patients.

Further reading and references

Back K. *Assertiveness at Work.* Maidenhead: McGraw-Hill, 1991.

Bramley P. *Evaluating Training.* London: Institute of Personnel & Development, 1992.

Hackett P. *Introduction to Training.* London: Institute of Personnel & Development, 1998.

Heller R. *How to Delegate.* London: Dorling Kindersley, 1998.

Markham U. *How to Deal with Difficult People.* London: Thorsons, 1993.

communicating
effectively

Glen Higgins
Practice Manager

Good communication is a key element in the success of any organization, and a general practice is no exception. In order to be effective, communication needs to be:
- timely
- relevant
- clear and concise
- open and honest
- consistent.

The benefits of effective communication include:
- an open environment that encourages dialogue and feedback
- good morale among the practice management team
- respect and honesty between team members
- slowing down the (often negative) rumour machine.

> **good communication**
> is a **key** to **success**

Leadership

There may be more than one leader in the practice management team – the practice manager, the senior GP partner and the senior practice nurse are common examples. In many practices, the practice manager will be seen as the leader of the non-clinical team, and it is the diversity and challenge of this role that make it such an interesting one.

It is helpful to understand different styles of leadership (e.g. directive, participative, authoritative). A skilful leader may have more than one style and will combine many qualities. The use of these will change depending on the group or situation they are dealing with. Some examples of leadership qualities and their uses are listed in Table 7.

Table 7

Leadership qualities

- Listening and learning – especially important when you are new to an organization
- Consulting and communicating at all levels helps people to feel motivated and valued within the team; also a priority when change is taking place and will help to dispel the uncertainty that change can create
- Integrity and respect – a good leader needs to be trusted
- Leading by example – other members of the team notice how the leader behaves; poor standards of behaviour will filter down through the team and give a negative message
- Supporting other members of the team will encourage respect and provide a positive working environment
- Confidence – lack of confidence will be interpreted as weakness
- Admitting gaps in your knowledge: this is not the same as lacking confidence; a leader who acknowledges that he/she does not have the answer to everything will gain more respect from the team than one who ploughs on regardless

Getting the message across

Communication can take many forms; deciding on the best method will depend on the message, the task, the team or person with whom you are communicating and the organization. The key considerations are how, when and to whom. The correct combination will ensure that a message reaches the target audience in the most effective way possible. The

communicating effectively

message must be clear and unambiguous, regardless of the form in which it is delivered.

How

Verbal

If the message is for an individual, then verbal one-to-one communication will be appropriate. This may need to be followed up in writing (e.g. on contractual or disciplinary matters). Clarity and lack of ambiguity are important in such situations.

A verbal message to a group is a powerful way of communicating news that affects the whole organization as it involves the whole team at the same time. Misunderstandings are avoided, especially if questions and discussion are invited.

Written

Written communication can take many forms, for example email, memos, reports, notice boards, the practice intranet. Email has become an increasingly popular way of communicating and can be effective in reaching an audience quickly. However, its popularity has somewhat devalued it as a means of communicating a serious message. A well-thought-out memo or report can carry more weight and may be taken more seriously by the reader. Remember too that not everyone in the practice team will read email regularly, especially if they work part-time.

When

The timing of communication is important. Messages about change need to be sent in advance to reassure, explain and solicit opinions.

> messages about change need to be sent in advance

Messages should be sent after an event to praise and congratulate the team or to provide feedback.

To whom

Decide on the target audience in advance – who is involved and who will be affected by the message; these are not necessarily the same people. For example, a change to the nursing team may not obviously affect the reception team but if the skill mix changes and the minor illness nurse is not available on Mondays, then the receptionists need to know so that they do not book appointments.

Listening and consulting

when **listening** or **consulting**, remember to give **feedback**

Successful communication depends on good listening and consulting skills. When listening or consulting, remember to give feedback. It can be difficult to reject ideas that arise from the consultation process and you must be prepared to explain your reasons for doing so.

Listening

Listening seems simple, but active listening is about using your eyes as well as your ears. When a person is telling you something, they do it with body language as well as with their voice. What the speaker is saying is important, but a good listener will also be alert to other signals, and will check and confirm that they have understood.

Consultation

Consultation cannot be underestimated as a tool for involving the team in decisions and events that affect the practice. It is essential if major change is planned; changes are more likely to succeed if everyone feels involved. In some situations (e.g. redundancy), consultation with staff is a statutory requirement.

staff consultation may be a **statutory requirement**

Running meetings

Organizing and running a meeting in general practice can be a difficult business – getting the right people together and having enough time to discuss issues properly can seem impossible. A well-run meeting will encourage attendance and participation in future meetings and is a useful tool in team building. Running a successful meeting depends on several factors, summarized in Table 8.

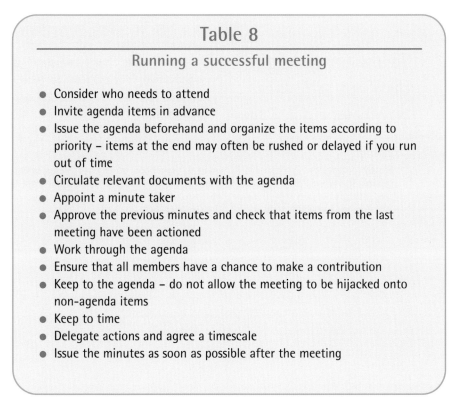

Table 8

Running a successful meeting

- Consider who needs to attend
- Invite agenda items in advance
- Issue the agenda beforehand and organize the items according to priority – items at the end may often be rushed or delayed if you run out of time
- Circulate relevant documents with the agenda
- Appoint a minute taker
- Approve the previous minutes and check that items from the last meeting have been actioned
- Work through the agenda
- Ensure that all members have a chance to make a contribution
- Keep to the agenda – do not allow the meeting to be hijacked onto non-agenda items
- Keep to time
- Delegate actions and agree a timescale
- Issue the minutes as soon as possible after the meeting

Organizing awaydays

An awayday is an effective way of focusing on a particular issue that affects either the whole practice or one of the teams within it. It can also be highly motivational and provides a good opportunity for team building. Attendance will depend on the topic to be discussed. Organizing an awayday is much the same as organizing a meeting, but the awayday provides time for a more in-depth look at a subject. Consider the following factors when planning an awayday.

- Who needs to attend?
- Off-site or on-site? If off-site, then how will the practice be run? If the meeting involves all the clinical staff, decide on locum cover.
- Funding: awaydays can be expensive. If the partners are not funding the exercise, approach the PCO. Pharmaceutical companies may also be willing to contribute towards the cost.

follow-up awayday decisions and plans

To ensure an awayday is worthwhile, it is essential to follow up and act on the decisions and plans made.

Further reading and references

Harvey J, Bateman C, Pittarides R, Simon C. *Handbook of Practice Management.* London: RSM Press, 2005. Also available online; see www.rsmpress.co.uk/bkhpm.htm

First Practice Management at www.firstpracticemanagement.co.uk

managing change

Janet Newman
Practice Manager and Writer

Change is endemic in the NHS, and anyone considering management in primary care can be sure that managing change will be an integral part of the role. In the last 6 years alone we have had:

- the GP contract, Red Book and items of service (IOS)
- fundholding
- PMS pilots, PMS+ and Alternative Provider Medical Services (APMS)
- nGMS
- PBC.

At the same time we have all been involved in the increasing use and dependence on IT; indeed, many practices are moving towards paperless practice (see case study 1 on page 120).

Often, change is seen as threatening. A good manager persuades people that it is in their interest to make the change and facilitates the change as seamlessly as possible. The keys to managing change are:

- understanding the change
- planning the process of change
- engaging those involved in the change
- completing the process
- keeping the vision.

To manage change successfully, there has to be vision; visualize your goal and work backwards from that. There also have to be incentives to urge your GPs along the change pathway; some GPs find it hard to understand that they have to invest in their business for it to succeed. As the management team of that business, you need appropriate tools to undertake your task of effecting change: a sound business plan, the

Moving into paperless practice

When we decided that our practice would become paperless, we agreed and set timescales and deadlines for each part of the process. This was particularly important for those doctors who were less computer-literate and were not confident that they could achieve electronic recording and consultation.

We set an end date – the date by which time everyone had to be recording everything electronically, no further paper notes would be pulled, and nothing further would be filed in the paper notes as everything would be scanned and filed electronically. In our case this was 18 months in the future. We deliberately set a long timescale as this was less threatening and seemed achievable even by the most computer-sceptical partner. In the interim we set stage dates – dates by which parts of the process had to be achieved. There were certain 'carrots' – incentives that went along with achievement.

As a practice we agreed to use a document-management system that ran alongside and was compatible with our clinical system. We arranged demonstrations from two companies who offered this solution at the time and then visited other practices to see each system in operation.

We trained staff on the new system; it was eagerly received, as the 'carrot' was no more filing in the paper notes within 6 months. At the same time we became 'pathology-linked': pathology results could be seen immediately, which saved staff countless hours of searching for paper results. Hence, the seed was sown and we were on our way towards paperless heaven!

We had already set a date beyond which no entries were to be made in the paper records, as we didn't want to run a dual system of entering information in both the paper notes and on the computer. Some feared the approaching date, but in the end we all achieved this target.

The next stage was not having the paper notes any more; convincing the staff to go along with this stage was the hardest task. We set a date,

3 months hence, when we would cease pulling the paper notes for consultations. One doctor insisted that he wanted to carry on having the paper notes, even though nothing had been added to them in the past 6 months. We explained that this was fine but, as the receptionists had all been assigned other tasks, he would have to pull the notes himself. Not surprisingly, he managed perfectly well without paper notes, as did all the other doctors.

The last stage date was when the doctors would no longer receive paper copies of their clinical correspondence and would action everything electronically – a scary proposition, but they have now been happily doing that for 2 years! In fact, using this method we achieved our end date with everyone on board within 12 months.

necessary resources and protected time for planning, meetings and visiting other practices.

Understanding the change

This is an often forgotten part of the process, but it is essential for an effective manager to understand as fully as possible the change they have to manage. There are many types of change, but in this chapter we focus on two different types of change that affect us on a regular basis:

> an **effective manager** should **understand** the **change** they have to **manage**

- change resulting from a government directive or legislation
- improvement change.

In both cases, background work is required before the implementation of changes.

The major tool of managing any change within a practice is a clear understanding of what you are about to undertake. Go to every workshop, meeting and conference you can on the topic. Gather information from websites, keep in touch with your peers and talk to your PCO.

Planning the process of change

Second to 'keeping the vision', planning and researching the change are vital processes.

Sifting the wheat from the chaff

If the change you are contemplating involves a process in general practice, you can be pretty sure that somebody is already doing it. Ask around your colleagues; use the practice managers' email forum (past questions are available from the fpm forum on the first practice management website); ask your PCO if a neighbouring practice already does what you would like to do, and if one does, spend time visiting and talking to the staff about how they went through the process. This can prove invaluable.

- Compare and keep comparing until you are sure you have identified exactly the right piece of equipment for the job, or the best process.
- Take advantage of the free demonstrations of products that companies offer.
- If the change involves IT, talk to your system suppliers; they often have preferred partners of software applications that are compatible with theirs.
- Shortlist your preferred options and engage with your partners and staff before making the final decision.

Engaging those involved in the change

General practice is a team game, and as such it is inevitable that any change within the practice will affect all team members in some way. Remember, change that seems small and relatively insignificant from a management perspective can have untold repercussions if the team has not been engaged in the process. The importance of communication in the management of change cannot be overstressed. Should you fail to inform the cleaner that you have changed the alarm system in the surgery, how will she or he secure your building after cleaning?

- Hold a partnership meeting to agree the change that has to be implemented using a business plan.
- Inform the whole team of the proposed change and, importantly, the reasons behind the need to change.
- Empower staff by gathering ideas and suggestions for the areas that involve them. For example, if you plan to refurbish a room in the practice for a specific purpose and group of staff, engage the staff in choosing colour schemes, layout, furniture and personal work spaces.
- Keep the staff up to date with the progress of the change by as many means as you can – newsletters, posters in the staff room, regular meetings, email or, in a small practice, simply by talking to the staff.
- It is important that the staff feel empowered and included. Be honest. Tell them what your budget is so that they don't have unreasonable expectations of what can be achieved.

be honest with staff

Completing the process – implementation

Once you have been through the process of research, planning, consultation, engagement and sifting the wheat from the chaff, the agreed change has to be implemented. Agree timescales and deadlines with everyone involved.

Managing change resulting from a government directive or legislation

Although the basic process for managing this change is similar to that outlined above, the management of timescales and implementation is often outside our control, and as a management team we usually have to contend with moving goalposts and changing timeframes. This can be frustrating, and hence this type of change is much more difficult to manage than improvement change generated from within the practice, where we are in the driving seat.

The change to nGMS and the QOF has been a steep learning curve for PCOs and practices alike (see case study 2).

case study 2

Managing the change to QOF

As soon as the new contract was on the horizon, various partners and I, as practice manager, went to every conference and workshop we could to gain the best understanding of the implications of the QOF.

Once we had a working knowledge, we planned two half awaydays and a team awayday to engage the whole team with the QOF. On the first half-day, which involved the partners and practice manager, we formulated some ideas for delivering the QOF. The second half-day was for the nurses and non-clinical staff. Here, I presented the outlines of the QOF and what it meant to us as a practice, so that every member of the team understood the QOF.

The team awayday was used as a team-building event to launch the QOF. After the half awaydays, everyone was asked which chronic disease area interested them. At the team awayday, each disease was allocated a table and the practice team was divided so that a doctor, a nurse and members of the administrative, reception and secretarial staff sat at each table. Each team was given scenarios relevant to their chronic disease that related to the QOF indicators. For example, when the diabetes team was presented with three generations of a hypothetical family with the disease and asked to create an action plan, they found that our questionnaire for new patients did not elicit the information we would need to achieve a good QOF score. As a result, we redesigned the questionnaire and also altered the way we record the information.

This proved to be a vibrant, enjoyable and thought-provoking day, with the whole team interacting and coming up with some excellent ideas very early on. We are convinced that the maximum QOF outcome can only be attained by working as a whole team.

Back at the practice we quickly formed the real teams, matching people to their identified areas of interest. Each team consisted of a lead GP, a nurse and an administration lead, as well as other staff who worked across teams, such as the phlebotomists, receptionists and secretarial staff. Throughout the year we have regular meetings of the chronic disease teams, as well as whole team meetings and audit meetings to look at the various aspects of the QOF. Many staff have learnt new skills and many carry out several different functions, providing much better job satisfaction and variety of work within the practice.

Implementation of the QOF has required a tremendous team effort but has been a hugely satisfying and worthwhile experience for all. Change can be rewarding and even fun; it is all down to how you approach it.

Evaluating outcomes

Whichever type of change you are managing, it is essential to monitor and evaluate the validity of the change. Change for change's sake can be demoralizing and destructive.

Several well-known management tools can be used for your evaluation, such as PDSA (plan, do, study, act) cycles, and comparative audit. The method for evaluating the change is not the issue; undertaking the evaluation is.

The engagement process must have an escape clause built into it. When staff are consulted regarding change, it is empowering for them to know that there will be a review process at some point. While you negotiate the change, assign timescales to the review process. It is far less threatening for staff to hear 'we will try this for 3 months and then review it' than 'this is what we're going to do, take it or leave it'.

assign timescales to the review process

Keeping the vision

Although it may sound clichéd, someone has to 'keep the vision' to drive through successful change. Although the process of change should be as all-encompassing and engaging as possible, the management team of the practice has to drive that change. Consultation is a vital part of the change pathway, but management by committee can stifle change and innovation. Keeping the vision throughout the process will focus minds.

Good luck!

Further reading and references

Harvey J, Bateman C, Pittarides R, Simon C. *Handbook of Practice Management.* London: RSM Press, 2005. Also available online; see www.rsmpress.co.uk/bkhpm.htm

The practice managers' email forum can be viewed and joined at www.firstpracticemanagement.co.uk

Some sources of inspiration:
- www.humphreywalters.com
- www.sapartners.co.uk
- www.oaklandtraining.co.uk

dealing with problems

Barry Coward

One of the attributes of a well-run practice is that the management team deals with problems raised by staff and patients promptly. Consistency is also important, particularly when dealing with staff issues, because what is decided today may well set a precedent for the future.

Staff problems

Staff problems can take many forms: a moan about not being allowed to take a particular day off; a personality clash; a question about whether someone is really up to the job; even a full-blown criminal offence. Some problems tend to crop up at regular intervals, while others will catch the management team completely by surprise.

It would require a thick handbook to address all the problems that may be encountered, but there are some general principles that apply to many of the issues that arise.

Communication

Many problems arise simply through a lack of communication. It may be a failure of just two people to communicate between themselves, or a failure of the management team to tell staff what is going on. This is very easily done; the management team can be so engrossed in a particular issue for so long that they forget to explain the fundamentals to the staff, who have no knowledge

> engender **situations** where **staff feel able to speak freely**

of what the management team have been considering. Misunderstandings occur, resentment sets in, people get upset and morale drops.

Management teams can also fail to consult the staff and glean their ideas, so changes are made without prior consultation, which again leads to resentment. The staff know their own jobs – seek their views, listen to their ideas, use their suggestions.

There are many ways of keeping staff informed, and also of getting ideas and feedback. It can be a mistake to keep the communications structure too formal and rigid. Informal chats can often be more effective, particularly if you want to hear what other people have to say. Many members of staff (often receptionists and administrative staff) are not comfortable in formal settings and will not say very much, so it is important to engender situations where they feel able to speak freely.

A blame-free culture

Cultivating a culture in which no blame is attached to mistakes engenders a far more comfortable working environment, and actually reduces the number of mistakes made. Everyone makes mistakes from time to time. Some mistakes may result from a lack of understanding, a lack of knowledge or a gap in training. Fill the gap, but do not blame the individual.

> do not blame the **individual**

A blame-free culture can be difficult to maintain at times, because it seems to be human nature to look for the 'culprit'. Unfortunately, it is becoming ever more prevalent in our society. The temptation to point the finger when things go wrong must be resisted and, if someone seems to be making the same mistake repeatedly, provide further guidance and remedial training as the first step.

Complaints

This discussion makes no attempt to provide a comprehensive guide to NHS complaints procedures, which seem to change about every 2 years anyway! Nevertheless, there are some common themes – the patient perceives a failing in the service provided and wants some form of redress, short of legal sanction and/or compensation. (The medicolegal aspects of complaints procedures are covered in the chapter on 'medicolegal matters', page 139.)

The investigation of a complaint is usually carried out by the practice manager. A GP or other member of staff often recognizes when a situation may lead to a complaint; indeed, the patient may have asked 'How do I make a complaint?' In such cases, it is helpful if the member of staff makes a written record of what occurred as soon as possible. In the case of a doctor or a nurse, a contemporaneous entry in the patient's medical record may also be appropriate.

It can be difficult if a patient goes to the front desk and asks to see the practice manager immediately after a situation has occurred. In some cases, it may be enough just to talk to the patient and perhaps offer an explanation. However, a really angry patient can be tricky to handle there and then. In such circumstances, asking the patient to have a seat in an interview room for a few moments may be appropriate, because a cooling-off period is often helpful. The practice manager can then also take a few minutes to prepare and, if needs be, have a second person present at any discussion.

Although it may be sufficient to hear what a patient has to say and make a written record during the interview, there is often merit in asking a patient to put a complaint

take a **neutral** **standpoint** when **investigating complaints**

in writing. By the time the patient gets around to writing, he or she will often have cooled down.

Unless the answer is absolutely clear-cut, the practice manager should refrain from responding to points that the patient raises in an interview. It is better to say that the matter will be investigated and a response will be provided in writing.

It is stating the obvious, but in investigating any complaint, the practice manager needs to find out what happened. It is therefore often useful to compile a chronological record of events, particularly the consultation record of the patient if the complaint is about a clinical matter. This can be enlightening. And it is often useful to include that chronological record as part of the response to a complaint. It can serve to put events into context, and into the correct sequence.

It is essential to take a neutral standpoint when investigating complaints. The patient's complaint may be entirely justified and the practice may, in some way, have got something wrong.

The final response to the patient needs to be carefully worded, whether the practice or the patient was found to be wrong. If the practice was wrong, the advice of a defence union on the appropriate wording can be very helpful and may avoid any subsequent litigation. (As an aside, there is a strong case for practice managers to be members of a defence union in their own right for this very reason. All the defence unions offer deals on staff membership if practice GPs are already members. The practice manager can then seek independent advice on the handling of a particular complaint.)

Technical, computer and data problems

In general, troubleshooting technical problems requires a wide and comprehensive knowledge of how the whole practice and its systems function. A good troubleshooter has first to be able to recognize that something is wrong and then find the cause. For example, the computers in four adjacent rooms appear to have no power, but the lights are on in those rooms. Knowing that the power points are on a different circuit to the lights will suggest that one of the switches on the main electrical distribution panel has probably tripped. If the switch can be reset and remain on, it is fine; if not, there is an underlying electrical problem on that circuit.

> troubleshooting requires comprehensive knowledge of the practice and its systems

To give another example, the practice may have a poor score in the QOF, which places great emphasis on data recording and the correct use of Read codes. This may indicate an area of genuine clinical weakness or it may be a data-recording problem. Careful analysis of how care is being provided and how information is being recorded may highlight problem areas and point to the solution; recording blood pressures or peak flow readings as text entries are the archetypal examples.

Unfortunately, running any modern IT system seems to be an almost continuous process of troubleshooting, whether it is a printer that will not print, a screen that has frozen or a whole system malfunction. Without doubt, comprehensive understanding of IT systems is an essential attribute for the management team. If the full depth of knowledge required is not immediately available among members of the management team, then a contract with a local computer consultant is invaluable. (This is over and above the support services provided by the clinical system supplier.)

In all but the simplest situations, troubleshooting a problem in the practice is a three-stage process involving:

- 'first aid' to deal with the immediate effects of the problem
- working with or around the problem
- fixing the underlying cause and any effects.

For example, a water leak floods the carpets in some rooms. 'First aid' involves stopping the leak by shutting off the mains water supply and, if necessary, draining the system; how many people in the practice know where to turn off the mains supply? Then, because the rooms are unusable until the carpets have dried out, room use must be rearranged, and furniture and equipment possibly moved. Then either the leak must be fixed as soon as possible, or that part of the water system must be isolated; the practice must have toilet and hand-washing facilities to continue working. Finally, the affected rooms need to be dried out and restored to working order, which could take several days.

Contingency planning

Some events for which contingency plans must be drawn up are rare, such as the loss of the premises (see page 82), while others may occur relatively frequently, such as staff absence through sickness.

Planning must not assume that senior management staff will always be on the premises; any contingency plans must work with just those staff who are always there, for example the duty receptionists. Thinking through how to deal with an event

no amount of planning can predict everything

that occurs at 6 pm, after all the management team have left, is a useful discipline. Checklists can list the steps that need to be taken.

On the other hand, no amount of planning can predict everything that might happen, and there will be occasions when members of the management team need to be telephoned at home for advice or have to return to the practice to help solve a problem.

clinical governance

Colin Tidy
General Practitioner

Clinical governance has taken on an increasingly high profile since the mid-1980s. With the development of Local Implementation Plans, National Service Frameworks and the QOF of the nGMS contract, clinical governance now plays a central role in every part of the NHS.

Clinical governance is defined by the DoH as 'a framework through which NHS organizations are accountable for continuously improving the quality of their services and safeguarding high standards of care, by creating an environment in which excellence in clinical care will flourish.' In practice, clinical governance requires that a practice constantly evaluates and improves the quality of patient care and services, and is externally accountable.

Clinical governance is not just a process; it is the development of a practice culture of quality and improvement. It should address all aspects of patient care and practice management. The culture of quality improvement needs to develop with experience, gradually incorporating a wider range of clinical and management issues within the practice. Each practice must progress at a speed appropriate to its own circumstances, otherwise all benefits are quickly lost, team morale suffers and the whole process will become difficult to resurrect.

> clinical governance plays a central role in every part of the NHS

Clinical governance must be a continuous process. It involves:

- identifying aspects of care that need improvement (taking into account local and national priorities as well as the needs of the practice)
- making plans to improve these aspects of care, using whatever method is most suitable
- monitoring success.

Concentrating excessively on one set of targets may distort attempts to introduce clinical governance in other important areas. It is essential that the focus is on the needs of the practice, not just on local and national agendas.

Addressing practice issues that are priorities is important for the future development and achievements of the practice. These priorities will be identified from team discussions, significant event analysis (see below) and patient surveys. Bear in mind that the practice does not provide care to its patient population in isolation: patients may be referred to secondary care, social care and other services, and thus clinical governance must include the effective use of these resources.

> **practice teams** are **most successful** when the **whole team** shares **objectives**

Practice teams are most successful when the whole team is involved and shares objectives. Each member of staff must recognize their role in providing high-quality care, and good practice management is therefore crucial. Clinical governance relies on a spirit of openness about problems in the care provided. A culture of blame has to be changed to one of open discussion, balanced evaluation, support and improvement.

Successful clinical governance requires a culture in which:

- everyone is included in the practice team
- the team is managed and led effectively
- the team is cohesive, open and mutually supportive
- team members are willing and able to acknowledge difficulties
- the team works together to improve performance and quality in the practice
- team members feel valued in their work
- personal development and education are valued
- the importance of the patient's experience of care is recognized.

Every practice team should have a member (not necessarily a GP) who is responsible for clinical governance in the practice. The clinical governance lead must have the confidence of the team and be able to provide leadership. This does not mean that everyone else can ignore the issue, however. The role of the clinical governance lead will vary in each practice but includes:

- working out a clinical governance plan, in collaboration with the team
- training for themselves and other key team members in quality improvement and clinical governance methods
- enthusiasm in helping to get clinical governance activities going
- identifying local sources of support, and acting as the practice link with the PCO's clinical governance lead
- reporting progress at team meetings.

The most important things to remember

Clinical governance is concerned with every aspect of the delivery of a high standard of patient care, but the most important ones are described in more detail below.

Risk management (practising safely)

Risk management applies to every aspect of a patient's requirements and experience of the care provided by the practice. Practice management is therefore as important as the clinical care provided, and includes:

> risk management applies to every aspect of a patient's experience of care

- telephone access for patients to make appointments, receive test results and hold appropriate discussions with healthcare professionals and the practice manager
- organization of clinical sessions and visits
- access to emergency drugs
- checking the credentials of locums
- effective and regular training for the reception team.

Developing information systems

Whatever the information system, effective clinical governance requires consistent and accurate data entry to ensure that data retrieval provides correct and useful information.

Audit

Audit provides the mechanism of a baseline assessment and monitors the success of efforts to improve performance. Audit must always be cyclical – it is only effective if all learning points are assessed, discussed, implemented and then reassessed at a later date.

Significant event meetings

Much can be learned from events that go particularly well or badly, and these provide an ideal opportunity for personal and team development. Significant event meetings will be beneficial in a culture of mutual support and development, but may prove detrimental if there is predominantly a culture of blame.

> ## much can be learned from events that go particularly well or badly

Learning from complaints

It is natural to be defensive about complaints; however, over-defensiveness will prevent any changes being made to stop the problem happening again. An effective complaints handling process should lead to a positive and constructive outcome.

Involving patients and carers

It is essential to involve patients and their carers; the practice should have a system for reporting comments made about the services or care received, and should carry out patient surveys (now far more widely used since their inclusion in the QOF). Patient participation groups can also be effective, but may be difficult to run and may not be properly

clinical governance

representative. They can also take a lot of time without providing significant benefit for patients or the practice.

Appraisals

Everyone in the practice team should be appraised, and the appraisal should cover all aspects of the individual's role within the team. An appraisal should be a positive process. In part, appraisals can provide an opportunity to identify the education and training needs of individuals, and are therefore closely linked to personal and practice development.

Data protection

Clinical governance requires the demonstration of high clinical and management standards to groups from outside the practice. This requires a good understanding of the requirements of the Data Protection Act (see pages 141–2).

Further reading and references

Harrison J, Zwanenberg T. *Clinical Governance in Primary Care.* Abingdon: Radcliffe Medical Press, 2004.

Department of Health, clinical governance: www.dh.gov.uk/en/Policyandguidance/ Healthandsocialcaretopics/Clinicalgovernance/index.htm

Clinical Governance Support Team: www.cgsupport.nhs.uk

medicolegal matters

Gerard Panting
Communications and Policy Director, Medical Protection Society

Medical practice in the UK is governed by a complex and frequently confusing legal framework derived from three main sources:

- acts of Parliament and statutory instruments
- common law based on decisions in the civil and criminal courts
- professional regulators such as the General Medical Council (GMC) which, although not empowered to make law, publish 'guidance' that, if flouted, can put the doctor's registration at risk.

The DoH and other bodies also publish guidelines, and practices have obligations to PCOs, PCTs and their equivalents in Wales, Scotland and Northern Ireland, with sanctions for non-compliance.

While ignorance of some arcane regulation may be understandable, ignorance is no defence. To succeed, the practice management team needs to know what is expected of it – dull though this is compared with getting on with the job of delivering care to patients. In such a short chapter it is impossible to set out a comprehensive account of the law governing medical practice and what practitioners and their staff must do to comply. When in doubt, ask first and act later. Practice managers will inevitably find themselves faced with numerous dilemmas on which they need to seek advice. For that reason, it is certainly worthwhile belonging to a medical protection organization in your own right.

> ignorance is no defence

This chapter deals exclusively with medicolegal issues. The general duties of employers, employment law, health and safety and other issues that apply to all businesses to which the public have access are discussed in the chapters on 'the legal environment' (page 31) and 'premises' (page 69).

Important statutes

Medical law may be a specialty in its own right, but not all the statutes that matter come with a medical label. To give some idea of the scope of legislation with a significant impact on the practice of medicine, Table 9 sets out a list of Acts of Parliament that are relevant.

Table 9
Medical statutes relevant to general practice

- Offences Against the Person Act 1861
- Perjury Act 1911
- Venereal Disease Act 1917
- Infant Life (Preservation) Act 1929
- Children and Young Persons Act 1933
- National Assistant Act 1948
- Sexual Offences Act 1956
- Mental Health Act 1959
- Human Tissue Act 1961
- Suicide Act 1961
- Abortion Act 1967
- Family Law Reform Act 1969
- Misuse of Drugs Act 1971
- Congenital Disabilities (Civil Liability) Act 1976
- Adoption Act 1976
- National Health Service Act 1977
- Unfair Contract Terms Act 1977
- Vaccine Damage Payments Act 1979

medicolegal matters

- Sale of Goods Act 1979
- Supreme Court Act 1981
- Supply of Goods and Services Act 1982
- Mental Health Act 1983
- Public Health (Control of Disease) Act 1984
- Police and Criminal Evidence Act 1984
- Enduring Powers of Attorney Act 1985
- Prohibition of Female Circumcision Act 1985
- Hospital Complaints Procedure Act 1985
- Surrogacy Arrangements Act 1985
- Aids (Control) Act 1987
- Family Law Reform Act 1987
- Consumer Protection Act 1987
- Access to Medical Reports Act 1988
- Health and Medicines Act 1988
- Road Traffic Act 1988
- Human Organ Transplants Act 1989
- Children Act 1989
- Access to Health Records Act 1990
- Human Fertilisation and Embryology Act 1990
- Health Service Commissioners Act 1993
- Family Law Act 1996
- Data Protection Act 1998
- Human Rights Act 1998
- Freedom of Information Act 2000
- Adults with Incapacity (Scotland) Act 2000
- Mental Capacity Act 2005
- NHS Redress Bill 2005
- National Health Service Act 2006
- Health Act 2006

Data Protection Act 1998

The Data Protection Act is a monster piece of legislation with wide-ranging provisions that place a number of requirements on all individuals and organizations who hold data about identifiable, living individuals. Specific provisions relating to medical records are set out in subordinate legislation (statutory instruments). Unlike its predecessor (the 1984 Act), the latest Data Protection Act extends controls to manual and computerized data files as well as placing more stringent conditions on processing personal data.

GP practices should ensure that:

- they are validly registered as data controllers
- they hold no more information about a patient than is needed for their medical care and use it only for that purpose
- records are stored securely and access is confined to authorized personnel
- patients' legitimate requests for access are complied with.

In addition, data subjects (those about whom information is held) have other statutory rights:

- to prevent processing likely to cause damage or distress
- to prevent processing for purposes of direct marketing
- in relation to automated decision-making
- to compensation for damage caused by a contravention of the Data Protection Act
- to request that inaccurate data be rectified, blocked, erased or destroyed.

Access to Health Records Act 1990

Much of this act was superseded by the Data Protection Act 1998. However, it is still relevant when applications are made for access to the medical records of a deceased individual. Following a patient's death, the personal representative and any person who may have a claim arising out of the person's death may apply for access to the health records. However, if during life the patient expressly stated that access should not be granted or there was some other indication that this would be the case, access should be withheld. The issue then has to be decided by the courts.

Access to Medical Reports Act 1988

This act allows individuals to have access to any medical report produced for employment or insurance purposes by a doctor who either is or has been responsible for that person's care. The patient must indicate if they wish to see the report before it is supplied to the insurer or employer and must make appropriate arrangements to do so within 42 days. The patient can refuse to allow the report to be despatched and can request amendments or add statements of their own. Copies of the report must be retained for a period of 6 months after it has been supplied to whoever commissioned it.

Adults with Incapacity (Scotland) Act 2000

In Scotland, people aged 16 and over can appoint a proxy decision-maker if they become unable to consent for themselves.

Mental Capacity Act 2005

In England, Wales and Northern Ireland, provisions similar to those of the Adults with Incapacity (Scotland) Act now apply, with full implementation in 2007. The British Medical Association has published guidance for health professionals.

Common law

Clinical negligence

Patients can claim compensation if they have suffered harm as a result of substandard care. The majority of claims against GPs result from a delay in diagnosis, but even in these cases, administrative glitches can contribute to or be solely responsible for the claim.

In a study of 1000 claims against GPs, 48 claims were associated with administrative problems in general practice:
- 18 related to administrative problems with the GP records
- 14 were linked with an error in communication
- 10 resulted from an error by a receptionist
- 3 stemmed from difficulties in obtaining a surgery appointment
- 3 were due to a lack of equipment
- in another 3 cases, the receptionist was to blame in some way but another administrative misadventure already applied.

However, looking at this breakdown rather underplays the potential for systems failures in practice. Reducing the risk requires proper induction training for all new members of staff, including temporary staff, and development of proper systems for passing messages both internally and externally, receiving and reviewing investigation results and acting on any abnormalities. A similar system must also be in place for all other forms of information received that may impact on patient care (e.g. change of medication following an outpatient appointment, repeat prescriptions, urgent appointments, referrals).

a practitioner should be able to justify why a protocol or guideline was not followed

Attempts may also be made to standardize clinical care by the application of protocols and guidelines. If protocols and guidelines are not followed, it does not automatically mean that the practitioner has been negligent but it certainly puts the onus on him/her to justify why the protocol or guideline was not followed.

Consent

This is an important issue, as failure to obtain valid consent before conducting any examination, procedure or treatment can give rise to complaints, claims and, in some instances, criminal prosecution.

Valid consent depends on the competent patient making an informed choice freely. The key is to ensure that the patient has sufficient information to make an informed choice and enough time to mull over their options before having to decide. Both the GMC and the DoH have issued comprehensive and lengthy guidance on the subject of consent, and all practitioners providing clinical care should be familiar with what is required.

Confidentiality

Confidentiality is usually regarded as an ethical rather than a legal issue, but that concept is now out of date. If there is a breach of confidence, patients may complain, sue for damages or both.

Confidentiality is another issue on which the GMC has produced guidance for the profession. While the basic principle is simple – patients have a right to expect that information about them will not be divulged to others by their doctors – without assurances about confidentiality, patients are likely to be reluctant to be open with their medical advisers. However, the duty of professional confidence is not absolute and the broad exceptions include disclosing information with the patient's consent, doing so in connection with judicial or other statutory proceedings where that information is required by law, and disclosures that are in the public interest.

The duty of confidentiality does not end with death, but following death there may be other justifiable reasons for disclosure of information, for example where information about the deceased person may be important to the welfare of the living relatives.

Complaints, complainants and how to respond to them

Complaints will be made in the best, as well as the worst, of practices. Some will be ill-founded, but in many cases the complainant will have a point that provides an opportunity to ask whether the practice dealt with the problem complained about as it should have done.

All practices should have a complaints procedure in place and every member of staff should know how to respond to someone making a complaint, including being able to explain how the procedure works and who within the practice is responsible for coordinating the response.

> every member of staff should know how to respond to someone making a complaint

Many complaints will be made in writing, but some complainants simply state their case at the reception desk. Anyone making a complaint verbally should be allowed to say all they want to say without interruption; however, for all concerned it is helpful to find somewhere more private than the reception desk for this discussion. The golden rules of complaint handling, whatever the circumstances, are given in Table 10; see also pages 128–30 in the chapter 'dealing with problems'.

Table 10

The golden rules of complaint handling

- Establish the facts before attempting to explain to the complainant what happened
- Explain the complaints handling process to the complainant so they know when they might expect to hear from you
- Once you know what happened, provide a full explanation to the complainant – verbally or in writing, as appropriate
- Do not be afraid to apologize: if the practice was in the wrong, for example by forgetting to make a referral or committing some other error, there is no point in explaining what happened but then denying that the practice could possibly be to blame
- If there is a threat of litigation, contact your medical protection organization as soon as possible
- No matter how vitriolic, offensive or threatening the complainant may be, do not rise to the bait! Remain professional throughout and then discuss the issue with your professional adviser

The NHS complaints procedure was modified in 2006 following the recommendations of the fifth Shipman Inquiry Report. It is anticipated that a single comprehensive complaints procedure across health and social care will be developed by 2009. Someone within the practice should have responsibility for ensuring that practice procedures comply with current regulations.

Professional regulators – the GMC and others

In all, there are nine professional regulators whose functions include keeping a register of practitioners, producing advice and guidance to the profession, overseeing educational activity and operating disciplinary procedures.

The GMC publishes a booklet entitled *Good Medical Practice*, which sets out the professional responsibilities of registered medical practitioners. The booklet announces:

'This booklet describes the principles of good medical practice and standards of competence, care and conduct expected of you in all aspects of your professional work.'

'Serious or persistent failures to meet the standards in this booklet may put your registration at risk.'

So, in addition to being aware of what the law requires, GPs must also understand the requirements set for them by their own regulator. One major issue which arose in 2006 was a proposal that the standard against which doctors should be judged in disciplinary procedures should be on the 'balance of probabilities', the civil proof standard, rather than 'beyond reasonable doubt'.

Revalidation

Another outcome of the Shipman Inquiry was revision of the GMC's plan to introduce periodic revalidation for doctors. The original idea was that doctors would submit evidence every 5 years to demonstrate that they remain fit to practise. The main body of evidence (for NHS GPs) would be the five annual appraisals within the review period. However, in her report, Dame Janet Smith criticized the plans for revalidation, and as a result there was a complete review of revalidation proposals culminating in the publication in February 2007 of *Trust, Assurance and Safety – The Regulation of Health Professionals in the 21st Century*. The revised proposals are more demanding, and include obtaining more objective evidence about the doctor's standard of practice and an appraisal system that is more summative in nature.

Chaperones

The Ayling Report, published late in 2004, concluded that the presence of a chaperone at a consultation must be the patient's decision, but should be routinely offered by healthcare professionals.

Having said that, the inquiry team recognized that some patients would not wish to have a third party present during an intimate examination, and that there are resource implications, as appropriate chaperones are not always available.

The team went on to recommend that no family member or friend of the patient should be expected to undertake any formal chaperoning role and that chaperoning should not be undertaken by anyone other than trained staff; for example, the use of untrained administrative staff as chaperones in a GP surgery was not considered acceptable.

Furthermore, the report recommended that each NHS trust should formulate a chaperoning policy which should be resourced and, in relation to primary care, should take into account one-to-one consultations in the patient's home and the capacity of individual practices to meet the requirements of the policy. Finally, the report recommended that failure to abide by the policy should be a disciplinary issue.

The GP contract

The new GP contract restructures the relationship between patients and their doctors, and between doctors and their PCOs. Patients register with a practice rather than with an individual doctor and PCOs contract with practices (as GMS providers) rather than individual GP principals.

The new legislation requires each PCO to provide primary medical services and to underwrite the new Patient Services Guarantee. PCOs can provide services directly to patients and commission care from non-NHS providers, for example where local services come under strain or there is no existing local provider. PCOs can also rationalize existing professional lists as there will no longer be a need to maintain separate lists of principals and non-principals.

Under the new contract, the money follows the patient. Thus, a reduction in the number of doctors within a practice does not adversely affect practice income, assuming that the practice's patient profile and service level do not also change.

Removal of patients from practice lists

The removal of a patient from practice lists is a contentious issue and one addressed directly within the GP contract. Where there is an irreconcilable breakdown between practice and patient, the practice retains the right to remove the patient from the practice list. This would normally follow an initial warning to the patient. Where a patient is ultimately removed, specific reasons must be given.

The right to remove violent patients is to be extended. Anyone who uses actual or threatened violence or verbal abuse that leads practice staff or bystanders to fear for their personal safety can be removed with immediate effect, provided that the matter has been reported to the police.

> if a patient is removed from a list, specific reasons must be given

Further reading and references

Department of Health. *Good Practice in Consent Implementation Guide: Consent to Examination or Treatment.* London: HMSO, 2001.

Department of Health. *Reference Guide to Consent for Examination or Treatment.* London: HMSO, 2001.

Department of Health. *Seeking Consent: Working with Children.* London: HMSO, 2001.

Department of Health. *Seeking Consent: Working with Older People.* London: HMSO, 2001.

Department of Health. *Seeking Consent: Working with People with Learning Disabilities.* London: HMSO, 2001.

General Medical Council. *Seeking Patients' Consent: the Ethical Considerations.* London: GMC, 1998.

General Medical Council. *Confidentiality: Protection and Providing Information.* London: GMC, 2004.

General Medical Council. *Good Medical Practice.* London: GMC, 2006.

Secretary of State for Health. *Trust, Assurance and Safety –The Regulation of Health Professionals in the 21st Century.* Command Paper 7013. London: The Stationery Office, 2007.

Silk N. What went wrong in 1000 negligence claims, Parts 1 and 2. *Healthcare Risk Report* 2000;7(1) and 2001;7(3).

Acts of Parliament: www.opsi.gov.uk

Data Protection Act: www.ico.gov.uk

Freedom of Information Act: www.foi.nhs.uk